Of all vital questions, none is more important than understanding of the acts and processes which ensure the perpetuation of life.

CAMILLE MANCLAIR

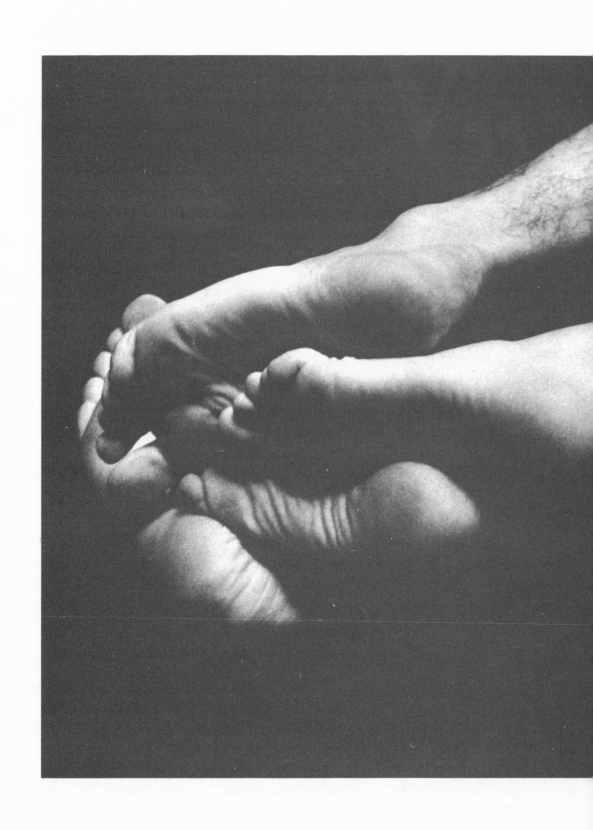

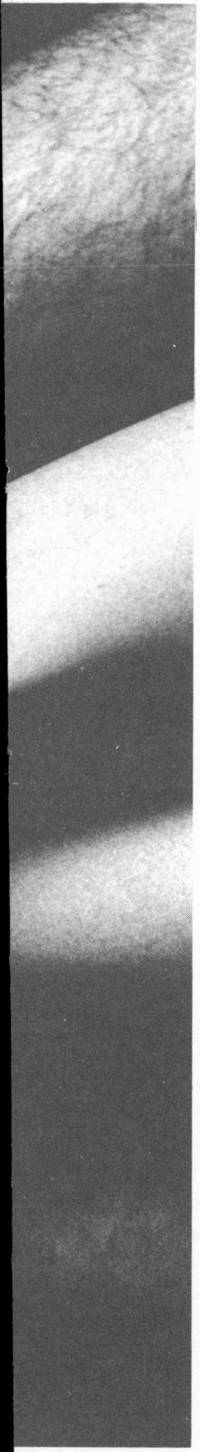

The
Picture
Book
of
Sexual
Love

PHOTOGRAPHS BY ARNOLD SKOLNICK

The Picture Book of Sexual Love

by
ROBERT L. HARKEL

CYBERTYPE CORP./NEW YORK, *1973*

Printed in the United States of America

contents

. . . and then I asked him with my eyes to ask again yes and then asked me would I yes to say yes my mountain flower and first I put my arms around him yes and drew him down to me so he could feel my breasts all perfumed yes and his heart was going like mad and yes I said yes I will yes.

FROM "ULYSSES" BY JAMES JOYCE

The
Picture
Book
of
Sexual
Love

1

The Building of Sexual Power

BANDON all inhibitions all ye who enter into marriage!" This should be the first and principal rule to follow in order to achieve a happy and successful sex life. Inhibitions are barriers between you and your partner—between you and complete sexual power. The many couples who leave these barriers up turn their sex lives into obstacle races. Don't let anything stand between the two of you. Don't let hesitations and anxieties keep you from complete sexual power and complete sexual satisfaction.

And the second rule is almost as important: "Know yourself." There are no general laws as to what is most sexually satisfying for all men. Every individual must look within himself, must test and experiment, to find out what he most enjoys sexually. So, know yourself. Know what sex means to you. Know what the perfect sex life means in terms of your desires, your pleasures, your needs.

You must remember that the degree of success that you have in performing successfully will, to a great extent, depend on how well you come to grips with these two rules. This is so because all that you are, all that you will ever be, is decided by the experiences that you came across when you were a small child. All the factors of growing up contributed: sucking at your mother's breast, being bitten by a large dog, listening to the wind rustle through the trees, the sight of your father knocking around your mother (or the opposite), and the thousands of other little incidents that make up every child's early life. This is how you were formed, and all these incidents have a bearing on your particular sex direction.

15

Every child experiences slightly or greatly different experiences. And every adult has slightly or greatly different sexual preferences and desires, as a result of the differences in early childhood experiences.

Do you prefer the breasts to the buttocks? Do you prefer a perfectly flat abdomen on your woman—or a cute little belly curve? Do you like long, skinny legs or shorter, fuller legs? Do you prefer long, flowing tresses or short hair on your woman? Whatever you like best, whatever is your particular dish—your particular preference will have been formed when you were very young. It is a waste of sexual power to try to change these preferences and desires. Live with them. Make use of them. Let them increase your sexual power. Change only those things which interfere with your sexual power.

To begin with, whatever fears you may have picked up from your childhood, from your parents—try your best to forget them. Not only do they have no place in successful sex, but they could seriously harm your chances of ever attaining true sexual power.

The woman—who throughout her childhood and adolescence —was told that it was wrong to have sexual intercourse (because she was not married) may still feel, deep in the darkest recesses of her mind, that it is still wrong to have intercourse —even now that she is married! Such a woman cannot give herself fully in a sexual relationship until she rids her mind of this feeling that sex is wrong.

The man who, as a child, was told that girls who have intercourse (or who perform other sexual acts, such as fellatio) must be "cheap" or "dirty" people, may subconsciously think of his wife as "cheap" or "dirty"—because she has sex with him! Feeling this way about his wife, such a man can never achieve a free and loving sexual relationship with her. Unless he can erase these irrational feelings from his mind, he will never have the ultimate in sexual power and he will never get complete satisfaction from his sex life.

The woman who for years was afraid of intercourse because she was afraid of pregnancy may still have remnants of that fear—even if she is using contraceptive pills! Such a woman can never relax herself completely during sex unless she can erase the irrational fear of pregnancy.

Children who were taught that it is wrong to "play with themselves" may feel inhibited from genital foreplay when they have grown up. Such adults may not be able to perform genital foreplay or, at least, they will not really enjoy the buildup to intercourse. For these people, a "quickie" is what sex is all about. Until they rid their psyches of the fear of (or distaste for) touching genitals, they will remain almost completely lacking in sexual power.

It is important that the fears, anxieties, and irrational feelings of sin or guilt, that were picked up in childhood—*but that have no place in a complete sexual relationship*—be eliminated. Without erasing these feelings left over from childhood, sex can be neither fully pleasant nor fully successful.

Erasing such feelings is difficult, as anyone who even slightly understands the working of the human mind will readily know. What your mind picks up is not easily discarded. What you think you have forgotten or, more accurately, what you think has been buried and forgotten, will very likely be stored away in the darker limits of your brain. Therefore, being realistic about what can and cannot be accomplished, you should try to wipe out at least those thoughts that will most interfere with the act of sexual union itself, regardless of what form they may take.

On the other hand, whatever "deep, dark desires" you may possess, make use of them—harness them! They are the fuel for your internal generator of sexual power. Dig them up and use them. How you may have picked up these inner cravings is unimportant. But the fact that they are there means that you must recognize them; to do otherwise means sexual frustration and unhappiness, and some degree of sexual failure. So let yourself go to wherever the desires of nature take you and discover your own unique ecstasy. No two men—or two women, for that matter—are the same. Each has his own individual lust. Thus, it is idiotic for anyone to "lay down the law" as to what is acceptable and what is not. Too often,

young people have been told by tribal leaders what form of sex, even what techniques, can be practiced and which ones cannot. This writer has seen many examples of this stupidity in the Western world, where dozens of books can be purchased, each written by an author who thinks that he, and he alone, knows the correct road to successful sex. Rubbish! Pure, unadulterated nonsense! There is no one road to sexual mastery. Such asinine reasoning is similar to that of the white Christian missionaries who spread out throughout the world telling local peoples what they should wear and how they should act—requiring them to live by their own narrow, stilted code of conduct. Beware of people who know all the answers, especially in regard to sex.

Every scientific study into the nature of sex has demonstrated that old assumptions about what is "impossible" are completely unfounded. For instance, dozens of self-appointed experts told women not to bother trying to be stimulated by pornography. They explained that it is absolutely impossible for women to be so stimulated. But scientific study has now demonstrated what common sense should have made apparent —that women, like men, vary from individual to individual, and that some enjoy pornography and some don't.

Another example: dozens of self-appointed experts declare that it is physically impossible for men to enjoy any sexual stimulation immediately after an orgasm. Well, this may be true of the experts themselves (or they may have convinced themselves that it is true) but it is absolutely not a "law." Some men never enjoy stimulation right after orgasm—but other men often or always do.

Don't let any tribal chief or sex authority tell you what you can or can't do. You must find out for yourself. You must find your own answers because only you have any chance at all of discovering your own secret desires. You are the only expert or authority on your own sex life.

At the same time, you must do your best to understand the individual lusts of your partner. Whatever goes for you goes for her too. What little secret cravings are going through her

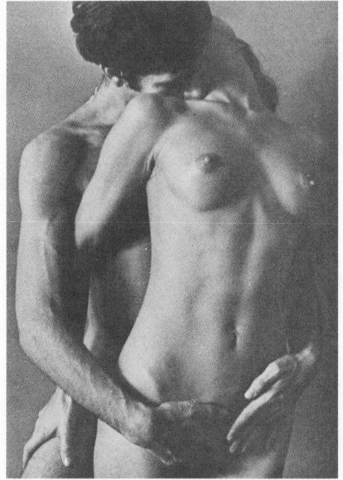

mind? What hidden hungers does she possess? If your partner is honest enough with herself, she may know these answers. Or they may be unknown to her and only you, after talking with her and learning of her background, will be able to unlock these secrets within her. Above all, experiment, probe, and learn. From experience comes knowledge, and with knowledge you can achieve almost anything. And remember: sexual experimentation is no dull chore; enjoy yourselves! The road to sexual power should be just as much fun as getting there. Don't just drive yourselves toward the ultimate in sexual satisfaction—that won't work. Stop along the way, exploring the byways of sexuality. Even allow your failures to be fun. Never be afraid of conducting a sexual experiment just because it may fail. Many failures inevitably precede a great discovery. Never be afraid of appearing foolish. Never be afraid that your partner may disapprove of your experimentation. If she does, so what? You are the man, and the man takes the lead in sexual union. And any form of sexual probing will, in the end, benefit both parties—and that includes her.

Remember too: make it as easy for yourself as possible. There are many tools that one can use, and the master of sex never hesitates to make use of them all. To ignore these aids is foolish and wasteful and invariably leads to sexual dissatisfaction.

Incidentally, you should remember to make use of a very valuable tool in maintaining a happy sexual relationship. Play "sex games" amongst yourselves.

That is, assume different roles in the period prior to intercourse. So, instead of the usual stale routine of engaging in intercourse in the set matter-of-fact manner before going to sleep, vary your approach.

Try the "Caveman" approach with your wife—not literally, by dragging her by the hair—by using a certain amount of force. In other words, play the dominant role to the hilt. Don't ask her whether or not you should do this or that—do it! Don't ask her whether or not she wants to do this or that—tell her to do it! Impose your will on her and make her enjoy being a woman, in the good old-fashioned sense of being the weaker, submissive sex.

Try the "Latin Lover" technique—using lots of charm and smoothness. Direct all your energies to pleasing her and only her. Get all your pleasure out of giving her pleasure. In other words, seduce her! Just because you're married and have experience with each other, you don't have to take your woman for granted. Conquer her, just as if you had just met and you invited her to your bedroom to see your etchings.

Try playing hard-to-get though not *too* hard-to-get! Your wife can try "Baiting the Bull"—that is, egging you on until you give her what she wants. The two of you may have gotten into the boring habit of jumping right into having intercourse as soon as you both are physically ready. Try keeping her waiting. Let her know that you will just go on and on with foreplay until you decide to—finally—have intercourse—or until she forces you to. Make her really want you before you take her.

Try mentally re-creating some of the more exciting sexual experiences you have had in the past—with each other or with previous partners. If there was one really great night on your honeymoon at Niagara Falls, imagine that you can still hear the thunder of the falls outside your bedroom window. Imagine together that you are once again in that motel room near Niagara (or wherever it was). Or make believe—together with your woman—that she is that blonde girl in the back seat of your Dad's car back in high school. Or that you are that sailor she met the summer before she met you. Let your imaginations transport you to other places or other times. Break the boredom by being new people to each other.

Play coy. Play for sympathy. Play that you're strangers to each other. Play that you're aboard a ship sailing to Europe or in a brothel in Mexico. But *play*. Let foreplay be fun.

There are all sorts of little "sex games" a husband and wife can play to make their life together more stimulating. Make up whatever games you can think of. If they're fun, if they make sex more enjoyable, then they're right for you.

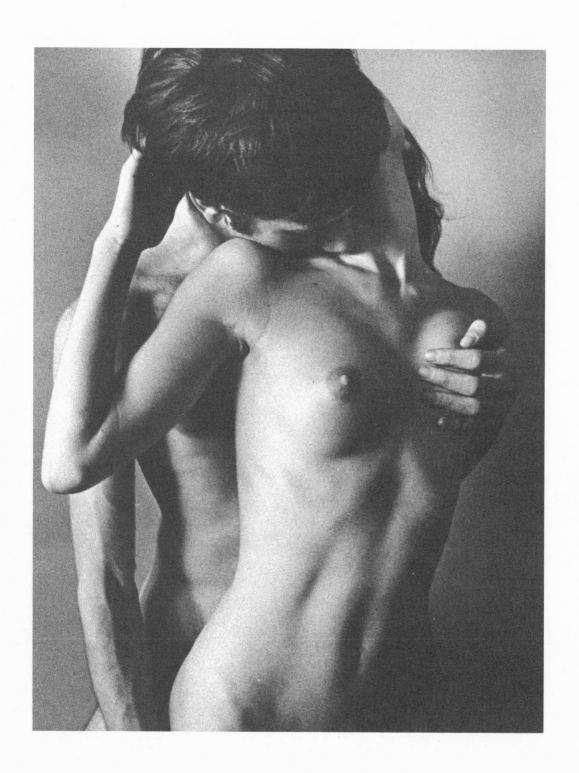

Look at your partner. Feast your eyes on her. Devour her body with your eyes. Mentally caress her beautiful buttocks, vagina, and breasts. Mentally caress the soft curve of her belly, the smooth skin of her neck, the shallow indent at the base of her spine.

There will be certain types of clothing that you like a woman to wear—therefore make sure that your woman wears this clothing. There may be a certain color or texture of material that arouses you—make sure that your woman knows what colors to wear and whether to wear silky clothing or soft, fuzzy materials.

Do you like medium-size breasts on a woman, or big, round bulging breasts? Most likely, you will have little desire for skinny women, but how fat do you like them? Pick out the woman who best suits your tastes. (Please don't be put off by the author's prejudice against skinny women. It is merely one of his personal feelings and has got nothing whatsoever to do with what you should prefer. Certainly, he has no intention of falling into the trap of what he has just been preaching about. So if you like them thin and bony and emaciated, then good luck—and have fun! After all, some skinny women make up for what they don't have by putting more energy into using what they do have.)

Let your woman know how much you enjoy looking at her. Watch her take her blouse and bra off; watch her body move as she slips her panties down her legs. Let her see that her every little gesture excites you. Nothing gets a woman ready to be loved more than the knowledge that your eyes (and your imagination) have already started fondling her body.

And let her look at you. You may or may not be Mr. Universe, but there are parts of you that look good to any healthy, stimulated woman. Women have imaginations, too: she can imagine what is to come as well as you can. And most women enjoy actually seeing how excited they have gotten you—even before the two of you have really started making love.

If you enjoy looking at your partner *before* the love-play begins, why starve your eyes once you've begun? You (and your partner) enjoy what you're doing—why blind yourselves to the act of love?

There is a widely held belief that women can't enjoy sex if the lights are on. Well, it's true that a woman may be bothered by the glare of a strong ceiling light. But a dimmer, shaded light shouldn't interfere with anybody's pleasure. In fact, most women will get an added kick out of being able to actually *see* what their bodies are *feeling* you do. And the breasts (or other parts) that get you so excited other times can be twice as wonderful to watch while they are below (or above) you, moving in the rhythms of love.

An excellent form of indirect lighting to use during intercourse is sunlight, streaming into your bedroom, filtered between the slats of a venetian blind or through your curtains. There is no reason why sex should be confined to nighttime, when both of you are tired from a long and exhausting day of work.

Sex isn't a sleeping pill; it can be twice as pleasant in the morning or afternoon as it is at night. And as long as your woman doesn't sleep with curlers all over her head and a pile of cream on her face, she may look her sexiest in the morning light. And you may be most virile after a night of rest.

Smell is very important—so make full use of it. Every man and woman has his or her own distinctive smell, which is sometimes pleasant and attractive, but sometimes, unfortunately, repulsive. We all know of the woman who prides herself on her own fine natural aroma, but in truth smells like the backyard pig. For a foul-smelling man or woman, there are fortunately artificial perfumes and natural substances which can be used to great effect. A man who sweats continuously, for example, would often be wise to use a deodorant and cologne—they are almost certain to give him a fine manly smell. But, of course, you must know your woman to know what smells and scents will stimulate her (or will turn her off, for that matter). Many women love the natural smell of a man's body—including fresh sweat. Of the colognes that can be bought in any store today, there are a number which have a bracing, tangy scent without having a sickly, sweet smell. (Lime and spice scents, for example, are particularly popular). Test out various colognes on your wife—there is sure to be a certain secret smell that greatly appeals to her, and creates a more masculine impression of you in her mind.

Women should experiment with perfumes and colognes; but, of course, she will always run the risk of smelling even worse than she smelled before—but this is a chance she must take. These ways and means of smelling better, naturally, are mentioned on the assumption that any man or woman will first wash himself or herself thoroughly. Soap and water can work many wonders. The smells that you find pleasant can almost certainly be traced back, of course, to certain associations of your boyhood. Thus, to repeat, harness these associations that are positive. Make use of them.

Remember, though: like everything else that has to do with sex, there are no universal laws. The various manufacturers of men's and women's cosmetics and perfumes spend millions of dollars every year to convince the public that natural smells are bad and only store-bought smells are sexy. Don't let anybody convince you that there are any such "laws." Some individuals prefer perfume; others prefer the natural smell of a clean body; some people even prefer a day or two's collection of natural body scents. And many individuals vary from day to day: sometimes you may prefer a natural scent and sometimes you may prefer a perfume. Sometimes you may prefer a subtle perfume and sometimes you may prefer a heavier, more obvious scent. Forget what the advertising industry may already have convinced you of; you are the only authority on what smells you like, and there isn't even any rule that you have to be consistent.

You may want to tie smell in to the "sex games" you play with your mate. If you are playing that you just met and are in a hotel room, you may want your woman to wear a new perfume she never wore before. If you are playing "Latin Lover," you might try wearing a stronger, more romantic cologne than you usually use.

In thinking about smell as a part of total sex, don't forget about your mouth. Brushing your teeth carefully before making love (or using a mouthwash) may make your kisses more pleasant.

Nor should you forget about the rest of the body. A dab of perfume behind your woman's ears may be just the thing when she's going out to a restaurant or a movie. But, in bed, there are many places on the body that can be perfumed besides the neck.

The mental occasions that make sound a valuable tool of sex often originate from our past experiences and background. The gentle rustling of leaves, the splashing of water, music, or the particular sounds of a person's voice, all have certain associations themselves. Sometimes a more robust sound will prove to be sexually stimulating. For example, the sound of a hard slap on bare flesh or that of a woman softly crying or loudly crying out.

The aphrodisiac quality of music has long been recognized. But the specific music that stimulates a person may be very different from the music that stimulates someone else. Some works have gained widespread reputations as aphrodisiacs —such as Ravel's *Bolero* and Stravinsky's *Rite of Spring*— but they may not stimulate everybody. Some women are most affected by soft, syrupy, romantic music. Others are more stimulated by the hard and driving beat of rock and roll. There are even people who are most stimulated by organ music. Find out which music relaxes and excites you and your woman —and then use it. Not just before having intercourse, but while you are making love, too.

If you enjoy seducing your wife—instead of just having sex as a habit—use music to aid your Casanova efforts.

Many people are especially stimulated by the sound of their partner's voice. Your woman may be excited by hearing you tell her just how great her body is while you are making love to her. Or you may be excited by hearing her tell you how much she loves making love—while you are making love.

And the sound of breathing plays a large part in the excitement of sex. You may use the sound of your woman's breathing as an indicator to tell you how excited she has become. Many people find the sound of panting or gasping a very stimulating part of the total sexual experience. Don't shut your ears to anything that may add greater pleasure to sex.

These are the sounds of sex. Make use of them. Enjoy them. All the pleasant associations connected with the sounds of sex are mental aphrodisiacs, and nothing is more powerful.

The Techniques of Touch Even though sight, sound, and smell contribute to sex, the building of extreme and utter passion very soon requires bodily contact and caressing. Here, it is important to remember that gentle stroking and soothing caresses build passion best at the early stages of love-play. Always be subtle and soft. The nerves which build early sexual excitement are gentle nerves, and, therefore, the silky touch is invariably irresistible and exciting. Of course, as you vary your approach from occasion to occasion, you may want to stress or play down certain aspects of love-play—but even a caveman has to know when to be gentle if he wants to excite and please his cavewoman!

All throughout our body, reaching everywhere, is an elaborate network of sensitive nerves. Therefore, it stands to reason that the most stimulating embrace will be between people who are entirely naked. It is obvious why this should be so. (And the most stimulating love-play is that which takes greatest advantage of this complete nudity. Do not neglect any part of your woman's body—and don't let her neglect any part of yours. There are numerous books that go to great lengths to prove that one or another part of the body cannot play any part in sex. Don't believe it!)

Complete nudity makes possible total contact between your body and the body of your woman. In this fashion, each body is stimulating the other; all the nerve cells on one entire side of each body are being caressed and excited. By undressing completely before a sexual encounter or during the early stages of intimacy, a total embrace that brings soft breasts against strong chest, which involves touch of soft thigh against tightened buttocks, belly against belly, or leg against leg, proves far more stimulation and exciting than an overly strong embrace. Complete nudity during love-play means complete and total sexual contact between man and woman.

All this is common sense, yet it is surprising how many people often hesitate in engaging in sexual union while totally nude. People who restrict themselves in this fashion must inevitably admit that they consider the private parts of the body to be shameful. How ridiculous! What could be more intriguing to a man than the tuft of hair by the vaginal opening? What could prove more exciting to the woman than the sight of a man's penis coming alive, growing and hardening in preparation for entry into her body?

To re-emphasize this point, because it is so important, it only takes a gentle, soft touch to stir the sexually sensitive nerves. Heavy pressure often merely deadens them. The clutching together of two nude bodies is merely one way— but it is the best way—of making use of many parts of the body to stimulate and excite the other partner. This accomplishes far more than only making use of the hands and the mouth—or only using the genitals. After all, if one or two points of contact can produce great sexual excitement and stimulation, just imagine what five or ten points of contact between the pair of bodies can produce. (Or, better than imagining it, try it!) Of course, just making contact is not enough. A gentle but unmoving touch can deaden the nerves as easily as a heavy pressure. Let your entire body move and explore her body. Use a gentle motion of your body, allowing more and more complete, overall contact with your woman's body. Contact itself is not enough. The contact at first must be soft, caressing, and gently manipulating the key parts of the body. And take your time. Love-play isn't a boring prelude to the "real thing"; it is part of the "real thing." Make the most of it—and linger over the joys of it. Savor it. And let a good thing last.

36

Kissing, of course, is generally the initial sexual encounter. Closed-mouth kissing with varying degrees of pressure, with moist lips or dry, with light contact or with assorted motions, will give pleasant and exciting sensations. This least intimate mouth kiss is sometimes underrated as a part of the total sexual experience. Even after a couple has progressed to deeper kisses or to more intimate relations, the gentle tenderness of the closed-mouth kiss should not be disregarded. At just the right moment, a closed-mouth kiss can lend that extra touch which can make intercourse a more personal experience.

Open-mouth kissing can be most interesting and complex. The tongue, for example, is packed with sensitive nerves. As this delicate instrument flicks forward, it caresses and rubs and tantalizes—exploring and so producing an infinite number of pleasurable sensations. Try, for example, driving your tongue deep into your partner's mouth, and then enclosing her entire mouth with your teeth, tightening around her upper and lower lips. This will hurt a little bit, which any woman worth a grain of salt will appreciate and enjoy.

Try exploring every part of your partner's mouth with your tongue. The crease where the upper lip joins the gum, for instance, is a perfect little pocket into which you can slip your tongue. Then slide your tongue down along the gum and over the front teeth. Some women are particularly excited by tongue tickling of the gums at the base of the upper front teeth.

Explore the pocket below the lower gum, where it joins the lower lip. Explore the underside of your partner's tongue and roll your tongue around it, up across the sensitive tip of her tongue.

Experiment with the in and out motions of both your tongues. Because a person's tongue is threaded with innumerable, highly sensitive nerves, the constant rubbing friction between two tongues can prove an exciting experience.

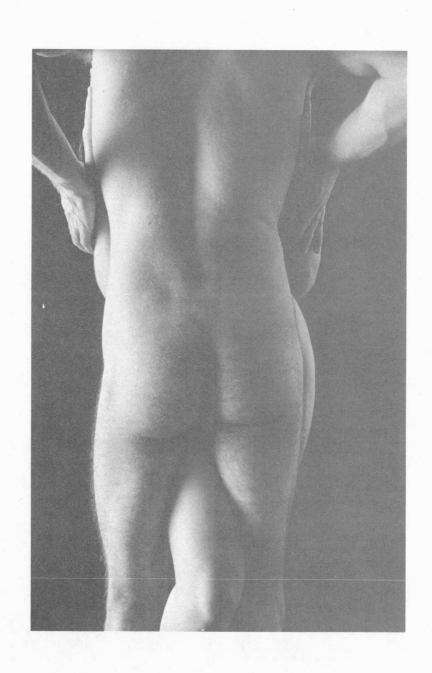

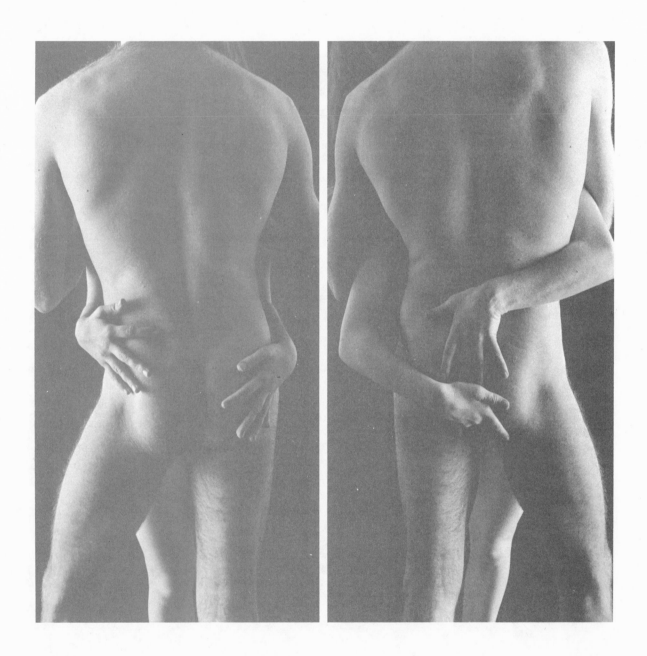

When your partner is exploring your mouth with her tongue, cooperate with her explorations by limiting the motions of your tongue. You don't want to push her tongue out of your mouth! A slight suction within your mouth may add pleasure to her explorations—but too much suction will only hurt her and force her to withdraw her tongue. Likewise, she will enjoy rubbing her tongue between your teeth, but be careful not to tense your jaw muscles and clamp down on her tongue.

From the lips, move on to other fields. Use your teeth—gently —to feel around her neck and, at the same time, encourage your partner to do the same. Nibble at the ears. This, certainly, is not to be missed. Almost everybody is deeply affected by having her or his ear kissed. But the exact method of ear kissing that produces pleasure varies from person to person. Try different techniques to find the right one for your partner. Get the ear lobe in your mouth and gently pull on it with your teeth. Pretend that you are stretching it. Or run your tongue along the ridges of the ear, circling lightly inward until you reach the very entrance to the inner ear. Or try encompassing the entire ear within your mouth. Then, with the ear in your mouth, run your tongue along and over the ridges. Try nibbling all along the rim of the ear. Or try driving your tongue forcefully into your partner's ear. Find out by experimenting—one way will have a powerful effect on your partner. It is your pleasurable job to find that way.

And now we come to the breast area of the woman. What a delightful area to play with! Here, so much can be accomplished, so many pleasures can be had, so much can be done to stimulate the woman. (And playing with your woman's breasts should be just as exciting for you as it is for her!) Use your imagination when you are faced with these two big beautiful breasts. All sorts of variations can be used in stimulating the breasts—and especially the nipples—with your hands and with your mouth. The mouth is most useful here, but this doesn't mean that you should neglect using your hands.

Gently cupping the breast in your hand is often an excellent prelude to more intensive love-play. Then gently caress the entire breast, moving your palm lightly back and forth across the nipple, feeling it begin to swell under your palm. Then, as you begin to concentrate on the nipple, play gently with the nipple, using your fingertips and the backs of your fingers. Circle around the nipple, using only the edges of your finger-nails or the very tips of your fingers, teasing the nipple. Finally, clasp the nipple between your thumb and the edge of your index finger, rolling the nipple back and forth gently. Some women enjoy having the nipple pulled—gently but firmly—away from the breast, stretching the entire breast. Others enjoy having the erect nipple pressed back into the breast. Yet others are delighted by having the nipple twisted like a screw. Try all of these techniques—and any others that might occur to you. Just as you are the best authority on your own pleasures, your wife knows best what she enjoys. She'll let you know which way of manipulation of the breast is best for her. But, no matter how much she may enjoy these caresses by your hand, she almost certainly will get even more pleasure from caresses by your mouth.

Here are several useful techniques:

1 – Try running the tip of your tongue across that little button on the breast. As you do this your lips should hardly be touching, while you lap at the nipple with your tongue. Remember, for this technique *only* use the very end of the tongue. You will, of course, be able to gauge the success of this (or any other) technique by the physical response of the nipple. Like your penis, the nipple becomes larger, firm, and erect when highly excited. If the erection of the nipple is lost while you are using one or another caress, then that technique is most probably not the one to use.

44

2 — You can try this little trick. Take the entire nipple area into your mouth, as if you were taking a moderate-sized mouthful of the greatest meat you have ever tasted. For this particular operation, you must tuck the tip of your tongue behind your lower teeth, and push the body of your tongue forward beneath the nipple. Then, push up the tongue so that it catches the nipple against the roof of the mouth. Then, slide it backwards and forwards in a gentle, sucking, milking motion. Do you understand how it works? For obvious reasons, this is often called "milking the cow." While you are doing this "milking," the top of the nipple will be passing back and forth across the front of your mouth's roof and the backs of your upper front teeth. If you press the nipple upwards hard with your tongue, this will add an extra sensation that most women enjoy. Or you may press upwards gently, concentrating on giving the nipple only the sucking sensation. Try it both ways to see which your wife prefers.

3 — You can take the entire nipple into your mouth and milk it between your tongue and the upper part of your mouth, just as explained in technique number two. However, the difference is that you are using much stronger, more powerful motions of sound, suction, and stimulation. As an added variation, you might also experiment with rocking the tongue from side to side, perhaps pressing the nipple up against the inside surfaces of your side teeth.

4 — Try putting your lips outward, so that the outer lines curl out as much as possible, exposing as much lip surface as you can. This is the surface that is soft and smooth and most useful. Place your lips against the nipple button very softly and

blow and suck. Cause the nipples to move in and out between your lips. Ideally, this should be done very quickly, but—this is very important—also very delicately and softly. Because this lip position is somewhat unnatural and because fast, extremely gentle motions are required, you may find this a somewhat tiring or difficult technique. Rather than using this technique badly (by being too rough or too slow), do it as gently and as quickly as you can for just a little while and then switch to another approach. You might take the nipple button between your teeth and shake your head gently. This gives a certain friction and, therefore, an intriguing stimulation. Or, if you like, try leaning your head away from the breast and thus very slightly and very gently stretching the nipple out. Almost any woman will greatly enjoy this. That very slight stretching action offers a woman an interesting little variation from the usual breast play.

5 — Roll your lips towards your teeth so that the latter are completely covered. Then, get hold of the entire nipple between these two rolled up lips and move your jaw from side to side. Also, roll the nipple between the two surfaces. This has the effect of "winding up" and "unwinding" the nipple button. Besides pleasing your woman, this motion will be especially stimulating and pleasing to your lips. (And, after all, caressing your woman's breasts should be just as pleasurable for you as it is for her to have her breasts caressed. In completely satisfying sex, it is always just as pleasant to give as to receive.)

6 — If your woman responded very greatly to having you stretch her nipple away from her breast (by pulling gently with your teeth), you might try

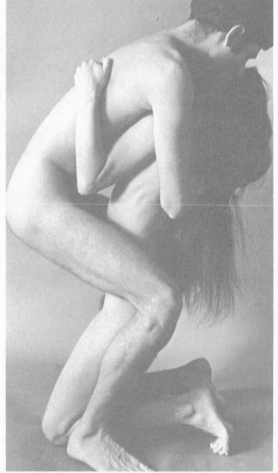

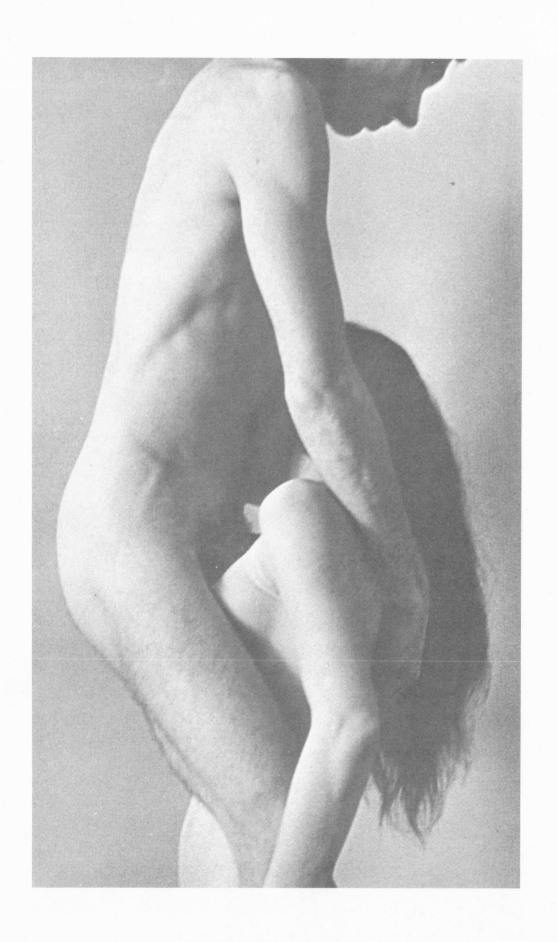

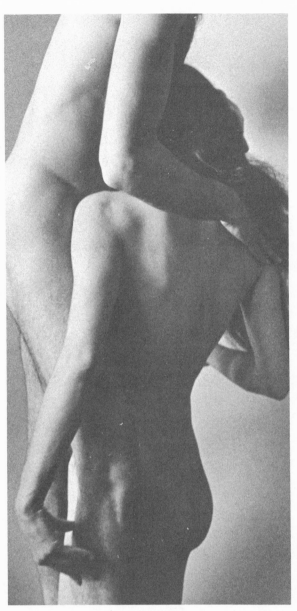

combining techniques four and five. With your lips covering your teeth, you'll be able to get a firmer grip on the nipple—without hurting—and stretch the nipple away from the breast even more than when you were using your teeth.

7 — Another technique well worth trying involves opening your mouth only a little bit and making your lips perfectly round, almost as if you were about to blow a smoke ring. Then, put your rounded mouth around the nipple and very softly and gently suck and blow, causing the nipple area to come in and out, in and out. (This is distinct from the other technique of stimulation of only the button itself with the teeth.) This is one of the driest techniques—the nipple touches only your lips, not your tongue or the inside of your mouth. For this reason, it is usually best to use this technique before others, so that the sensations of this stimulation are not blurred by wetness. Of course —as this writer has said over and over—every individual has his own preferences, and some people prefer using this as a wet technique. You might try it both ways, to see which you and your wife like best.

8 — Stretch out your tongue and lay the surface flat against the nipple. Then, very softly rub it back and forth, around and around, and then across and back again in a variety of motions. Use the flat top of your tongue, the tip, the sides, and the underside of your tongue. Each part of the tongue causes a different type of sensation, and the best caress is made of a combination of these sensations. Nor do you have to concentrate only on the nipple. You can move around the breast, especially trying the very base of the breast. But, of course, the nipple area is the most sensitive part

of the breast and you should always return to this lovely button and the sensitive area just around it.

9 – You have to be careful not to really bite down on the nipple—this will cause extreme pain and will probably ruin your partner's appetite for further sex. But nibbling carefully will do much to excite and stimulate most women. The nipple itself is best for nibbling—although some women will enjoy you nibbling all over the breast. If your wife gets a special excitement from your nibbling at her nipple with your front teeth, you might also try gently chewing on the nipple with your molars, rolling the nipple around on the broad surfaces of these chewing teeth. As a final extra sensation, use your canine teeth (the sharp, pointy teeth next to your front teeth), to nip down —sharply, quickly, but still gently enough that you do not cause more than a drop of pain. Any woman who really enjoys having her breasts stimulated—which is to say, any woman worth making love to—will enjoy the little, sharp jab of pain caused by this nip, but you must be careful not to cause too much pain.

While you are caressing one breast with your mouth, there are any number of things that you can be doing with your hands. If you are using suction, or "milking," techniques, it is often a good idea to use your hands to cup the breast, kneading and pulling the breast, while holding it so that you can comfortably do whatever you want to do to the nipple. Or your woman may want to cup her breast for you, offering the nipple to you for your pleasure. If she does this, you will still have your hands free for other caresses.

You may want to manipulate one breast while you are caressing the other with your mouth. If your mouth—your lips or teeth —is stretching one nipple from its breast, you can imitate this action on the other nipple, using your thumb and index finger.

Of course, there is usually no reason to just single out one breast for all your mouth-play. You can switch back and forth from breast to breast, keeping both in a state of high excitement. If you dally over one breast, you can use your hand to keep the other nipple erect until you get back to it. Or you can be caressing other parts of your wife's body while you picnic on her breasts. One hand might lightly wander over her thighs or begin a light stimulation of her vaginal area while you caress her breasts with your mouth. In some positions, you will even be able to lightly massage and tease her buttocks while your mouth is on her breast.

Caresses of the breasts are often part of the early stage of love-play. And playing and loving your woman's breasts *is* an excellent beginning. But there is no reason for you to neglect the breasts later in the love-play. As a matter of fact, you shouldn't always do the same things in the same order every time you have sex. Pity the poor woman whose man treats her like an assembly-line machine, on which the levers must always be pulled and the buttons pushed in the same mechanical order. Such a man lacks imagination—and imagination is an important part of sexual power.

Try caressing the breasts while you are having intercourse. Or caress the breasts *after* caressing your woman's vaginal area. Or even after the climax.

And there should never be a set time limit: one night you may spend only a few moments on the breasts; another time you might leisurely make love to your woman's breasts for twenty or thirty minutes. Many women are able to achieve an orgasm just by having their breasts caressed!

There are, of course, other important parts of the body. You and your partner will find that gentle caressing produces excitement most acutely by the ears, hair, shoulders, lower stomach, the back, the crotch, creases of the buttocks, and wherever your desire or fancy takes you both.

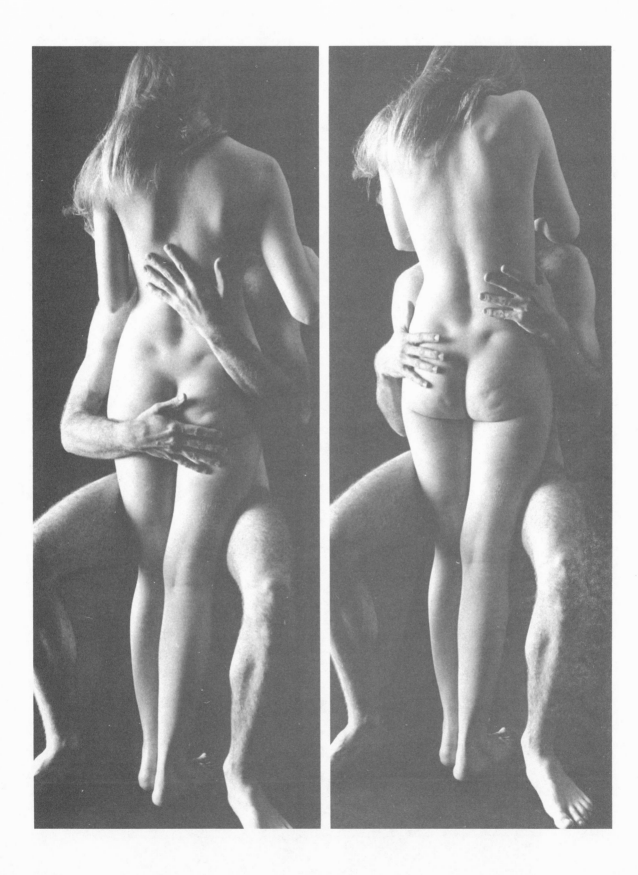

You might commence your bare-skin embrace as soon as possible and rub, stroke, and twist against each other as much as possible. Your woman may want to lower her crotch onto your bent knee, squirming her entire body to produce the most exciting sensations in her genital area. You might want to gently run your penis along her legs or across her buttocks or belly—or even higher, between her breasts, which she may want to move back and forth across your male organ.

Don't produce pain at this early period; just be gentle and soft. Always be sure to keep your hands moving, always moving, because they are your most versatile tools. To a great extent, the speed with which excitement mounts between you and your partner will depend to a certain amount on how successfully you put your hands to a good use.

(But, of course, don't think of sex as a race to the finish. Even though you want the level of excitement to mount as rapidly as possible, you should take your time and enjoy the excitement you achieve.)

After a short while, you might try bunching your fingertips together. Use them to stretch the skin over a sexually sensitive area, such as the lower back. Move them back and forth, side to side, and even around in a circle as far as possible so the skin will stretch. Experiment with the lower back and other tight-skin areas to find which is most sensitive on your woman. This varies greatly from individual to individual. There are women who can be brought to great heights of excitement and desire merely by manipulating the skin of their lower back. On the other hand, there are women who are left completely cold by this technique. The only way to find out which group your woman belongs to is to experiment. If she is one who is greatly excited by this kind of play, you won't have to ask her: she'll let you know—her whole body will let you know—the first time you try it!

Then go hunting for a plumper area of flesh, such as the buttocks, and grasp hold of quite a substantial area with your thumb and fingers, then clutch it and almost mold it as if it were a piece of dough. Play with it, stretch it, mold it, then press it into the flesh with your fingertips. Remember: don't cause pain, because this is not the time. Just remember to be firm. Many women especially enjoy being firmly grasped on their sides, at the waist—just above the hips. And many enjoy lying face down as you firmly grasp a buttock in each hand and move your hands in a sure, rhythmic pattern: up and down, side to side, in a circle, and then in two circles—each buttock being rotated opposite to the other. Some women will enjoy the same thing being done to their breasts as they lie relaxing on their back.

Then, separate the fingers and claw at the flesh, particularly around the upper parts of the breasts, neck and sides. You might find that the hips are highly sensitive.

Or draw your fingernails—not too roughly, of course—along the soft skin of the inner thighs.

But it all boils down to the peculiarities of the individual person. Some women are visibly excited by kissing of the back, yet are not in the least bit responsive to gentle touches applied to this part. Women, then, can and do have different attitudes towards kissing and stroking—all caused, no doubt, by the inner psychological quirks with which they regard these particular forms of stimulation.

Remember, an essential part of all this is surprise and variety. Therefore, try all sorts of new little tricks to surprise and delight your partner. Try pounding your fist on the back of your partner, rake your nails across the skin, sink your teeth into the fleshy parts of the body (though, remember, not so hard as to cause intense pain), and generally do anything you feel like doing—or anything your woman suggests that you try on her—just for the fun of it.

Never forget that the worst thing that could happen to sex play is dull routine; letting yourself degenerate into a mechanical lover who follows a dull, boring (and bored) pattern. This becomes deadly, but the frightening thing is that so many people who have fallen into this trap are often not

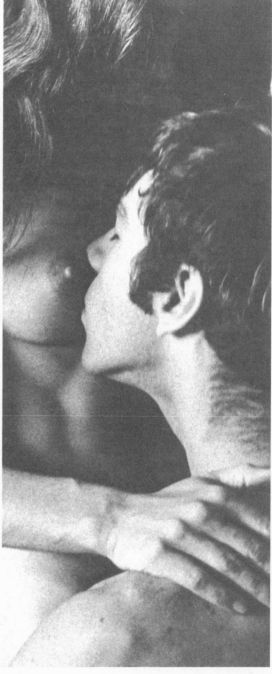

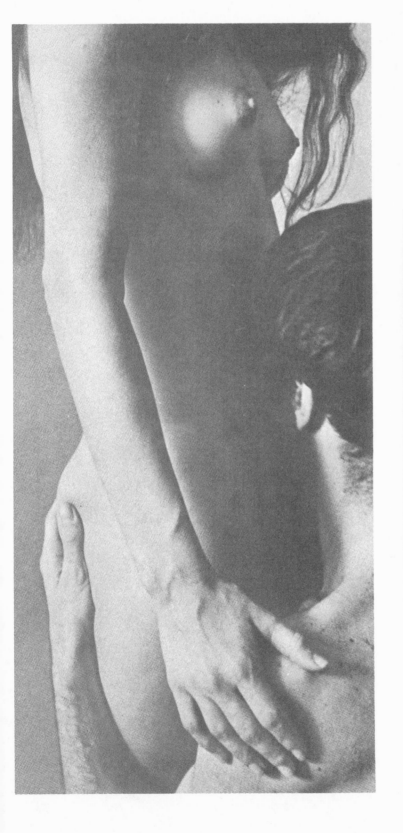

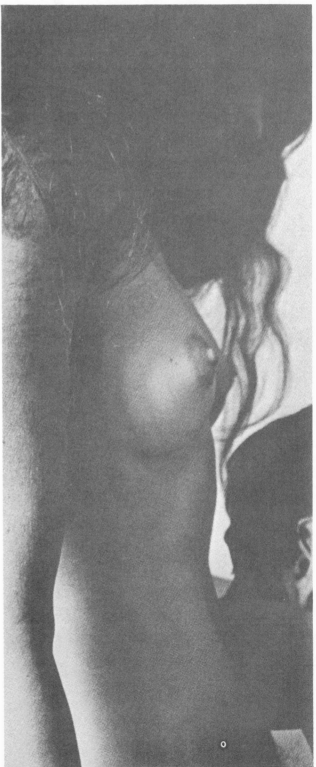

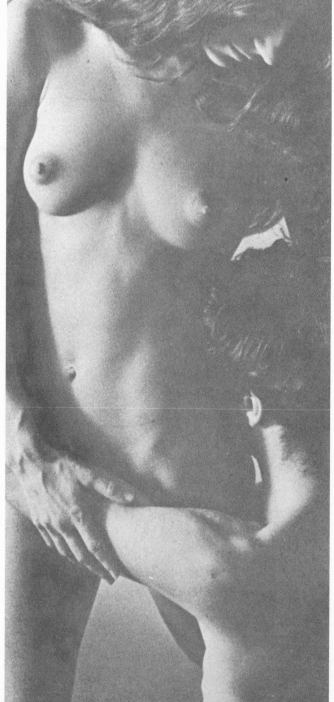

aware of what has happened to them. All they know is that, somehow, sex is just not as interesting as it used to be. And uninteresting sex makes about as much sense as dry water. If sex isn't fun, it isn't anything at all.

A further area to try—and an area that is often neglected— is the stomach. Work around the area of the navel by any means of stimulation you wish—massaging it with your fingertips, licking with your tongue, brushing the area with your lips, or making little nibbling motions with your lips or teeth. At any rate, a great degree of stimulation can often be worked up by playing in this area. Then, move down a bit to the areas on the inner sides of the hip bones. This area particularly responds to stimulation. Depending on the particular sensitivities of the woman, you will probably find that it is necessary to use a firmer, more vigorous touch. Light sensitive strokings merely tend to tickle—and this is certainly not what you want. Nearby are the inner thighs, and they most definitely deserve your leisurely attention. Here, you may move your fingers around, carefully kneading the skin. Too firm a hand may just dull the sensations here, though. You might try using your fingertips here, letting them dance so lightly on the skin that you almost can't feel the thighs with them. Or brush the area with your lips, as you did with the stomach. The nibbling motions you used on the stomach probably won't work here, but you might as well try it once, just to find out. Stimulate the entire thigh area, right from the little creases beside the vagina's outer lips down to the inside crease of the knees. This entire delightful area is, of course, very important because it is usually one of the "jumping off points" towards your final, climactic conquest. Here, of all places, don't become impatient. Take your time and make good use of the sensitivity of this area to bring your woman to the highest possible stage of excitement before going further. You will be rewarded greatly for every extra bit of excitement you produce for your woman at this stage of the love play.

An important part of any sexual stimulation is, of course, massage. Basically, a massage serves two purposes: to relax the muscles and to sexually arouse the body. In addition, the giving of a long, loving massage is a sexual "present," which will make the recipient not only "hotter," but also more desirous of returning the "present" in increased sexual vigor later in the love-play. (And it can be very exciting to *give* such a massage, playing with and wandering over the relaxed body of the partner!)

To receive this very delightful form of "treatment" (or "treat"), first lie down flat on your stomach, with your arms in a comfortable position away from your torso, and have your wife begin at the base of the skull. Have her place her fingers in one spot and move them around in a circular fashion, stretching the skin. This should be done under the ears (one hand massaging the area under each ear, of course) and at the very back of the neck, as well as the shoulders. Here, emphasis should be on her thumbs as she goes over your muscles in this circular fashion. The palms of her hand can be used, rubbing against the skin, to produce the warmth that relaxes the back muscles. The base of the palm will be especially effective in applying pressure to muscle knots. Before moving down the back, your wife should be sure that she has completely relaxed all the muscle tightness in the neck and shoulder area. As long as these muscles remain tight, the complete relaxation of other back muscles will be impossible. If necessary, she may pound—not too hard, of course—at muscle tightness in the shoulders, using the pinkie-edge of her hands, or even using closed fists. A quick, not-too-gentle skin rub will also be effective on the shoulders, to produce relaxing warmth.

The spine is very important, as much of your tiredness will be centered in your back. (It will help a great deal if she uses some kind of oil.) The small of the back, the base of the spine, and the areas beside the small of the back are also quite important. These areas call for a little more gentle

65

action than the shoulders, but complete relaxation is impossible if these areas are not relaxed as fully as the neck and shoulders. Other than oil, a very good substance to use in back massages is alcohol. As the alcohol evaporates, it causes a cooling sensation which is very pleasant after the warming sensations of rubbing. Some people also enjoy a quick, light, talcum rubdown after an alcohol massage.

Then, down to the buttocks, thighs, legs, ankles, and feet. The calves are often very tight, and this tightness is a cause of fatigue. Here, your wife should use a firm, grabbing—and rubbing—motion with her full hand. She should concentrate pressure with her thumb and the base of her palm. If these muscles are knotted, hard and fast skin-rubbing will begin their relaxation. Your wife may also have to use the same pounding action here as on the shoulders, perhaps even harder than she used there. In doing the feet, a hard, kneading action of the knuckles into the arch of the foot will be especially good. Your wife should also stretch each toe away from the foot—firmly, but not too hard.

At this point, you turn over and she begins at the top again. She may gently massage your temples and your face muscles before doing a very gentle neck message. Most women enjoy rubbing a man's muscular chest, and you will enjoy it if she is gentle, but firm. And so on down the body. Naturally, you should make sure that she doesn't excite you too much—after all, a massage is only the "first course" of your sexual feast. But if your wife does her job properly, the tightened knots of your body should be relaxed and loosened. And you should be ready to use all your sexual power to reward your wife for a massage well done. And remember: a good way to begin a massage is to first take a hot bath or hot shower. This way, your pores are open and your muscles are already partially relaxed to begin with.

While a hot bath or shower is a perfect preparation for a massage, a "love massage" can actually *begin* in the shower or bath.

68

Showering or bathing together can be a perfect beginning for an evening devoted to love-making. As a matter of fact, some couples will enjoy holding their complete love-fest under the stimulating hot spray of a shower.

Wash each other. Your hand on your woman's body can be twice as stimulating to her when she is covered with soap suds. The hand slips and slides across the soapy skin, finding its way into every crevice and onto every curve. Washing her back vigorously will relax her. You can do it with one hand while your other hand supports her body by firmly caressing one of her breasts. And don't forget to wash her breasts! The actions of your hand made more gentle by the soapy water will excite her to new heights. Any woman worth her salt will want you to wash her genital area. Just be sure you use a mild soap so that you don't cause irritation.

And encourage your woman to wash you. Let her take her time washing your back and your chest and stomach, but don't let her get tired before she reaches your genitals. Make sure she is gentle when she washes your scrotum—and be sure that she uses a mild soap—but let her go to town washing your penis. Just remind her that if she washes *too* well, you'll be all washed up for a while.

Usually after a love-massage in the shower, a couple will want to retire to the comfort of the bedroom. But once in a while, try completing relations right in the tub. The relative discomfort of the hard bottom of the tub and the cramped conditions is a small price to pay for this exciting change in your sex routine.

2

Sexual
Stimulation

N

ow we come to the heart of the matter! Here is the region which decides everything. Here is your main and final test, on which you either stand or fall, that lets your woman know whether she is in the hands of an amateurish boy or a man who is fully in control of the situation. Remember to take your time—at least fifteen minutes, preferably more—and keep full control of yourself. You will already have reached a high plateau of excitement—don't go any further! Hold your own excitement back now, relax your sexual tension a little, and concentrate on pushing your woman to greater heights.

Display no hesitancy: a woman is sure of a man who is sure of himself. But also display no impatience. Your body may be craving deeper fulfillment of its desires, but control yourself. Let it be your woman who craves you, who demands you, who pleads for intercourse. For a little while now, forget your own needs and concentrate on making yourself needed.

Keep in mind that every part of your woman is fair game, a perfectly legitimate target for whatever you want to do. Thus, it will be your task to overcome whatever inhibitions she might possess—and you will only accomplish this by being firm and uncompromising. Of course, you must remember that there is a world of difference between firmness and brutality. It is the sexually weak man who finds it necessary to force his will on his woman, without any regard for her feelings or the crassness of his own aggressiveness. The strong can always be gentle: the sexually powerful man is firm without being brutal. He knows what is best for himself and his partner, and he is firm and steady in achieving what he knows must be achieved. He uses his sense of confidence and his sureness to sway his weaker-willed partner. But he never plays the rapist: overpowering an unwilling and frightened wife.

You can afford to yield to your woman's reluctance to allow you to perform one or another sexual act—for a few nights! But after that you must conquer. Every sexual encounter must be a pitched battle between your sureness and her timidity. It isn't your wife that you must defeat: it is her fears that you must annihilate. And annihilate them you must! After all, *you* know what is best for her—because what is most desirable for either of you is always best for the other. What you want is automatically best for her.

Keep in mind one thing above all else: nothing is more pitiful, pathetic, and even contemptible than a man who yields his position of masculinity to his woman. He is abandoning his fight and allowing himself to be led by his woman—something which no normal man can ever possibly tolerate. Nor can any normal woman long tolerate a man who refuses to be the man. Your woman wants to be led; she wants to be conquered. Deep within her, she wants you to eliminate her fears and overcome her inhibitions and her timidity. She wants to be a woman—and she can only be a woman if you are really a man.

On the other hand, there is no reason for you to disregard your woman's desires. If there is something she enjoys and wants you to do to her—if she lets you know of a technique or a sexual action that will enhance her excitement—be grateful for her frankness, *and do it!* Even after years of marriage, many wives feel embarrassed about asking their husbands to please them in a particular way. It is your job to make sure that your wife rids herself of this foolish modesty. So, be sure to reward her whenever she overcomes her natural timidity and tells you what she secretly desires. Do what she ask, and be happy that you have helped your partner overcome her inhibitions.

When a man begins to caress and stimulate the clitoris, the tissues are usually dry. Thus, it will be very important that you realize that your woman will feel a slight irritation before the clitoris becomes moist, either through any lubricant you might use or through natural secretions. It stands to very good reason, therefore, that you should use no frictional stimulation at the beginning. You want to excite the clitoris, and an irritated clitoris is often almost impossible to really excite. Throughout your love-play, you will have to keep this in mind, but it is an especially important consideration at the very beginning of your caresses of the genital area. This is one reason why it is always best to take your time in building your woman's excitement *before* caressing the clitoris. If your woman is already very excited, the genital area will have already begun to lubricate itself; your first approach to the clitoris will help spread this natural lubricant up from the vagina to the object of your caresses.

In any case, it is best to begin your attentions to the clitoris gently and carefully. The skin of the clitoris is most sensitive, and your fingers must run smoothly over this part. So you can try four useful methods:

1 — You can roll your finger back and forth across the tip of the base of the clitoris in a rolling motion. But remember: this must be done lightly; and it is important that your hand be clean— not only for health reasons, but also because salt, acid, or dirt will irritate this highly sensitive love knob.

2 — Or, you can use a slightly vibrating stimulation. This is done by jiggling the finger over the clitoris without moving over any area (so to cause friction). In this way the surface moves with the finger as the skin stretches.

3 — You can use two fingers to stimulate the clitoris without chancing irritation. Gently place one finger on either side of the clitoris, forming a soft

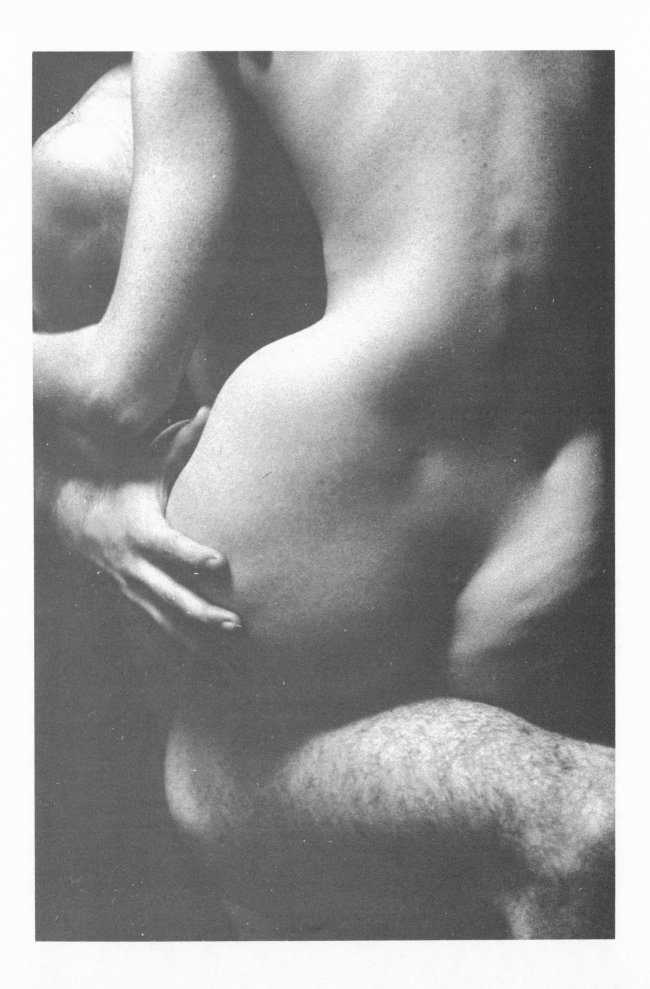

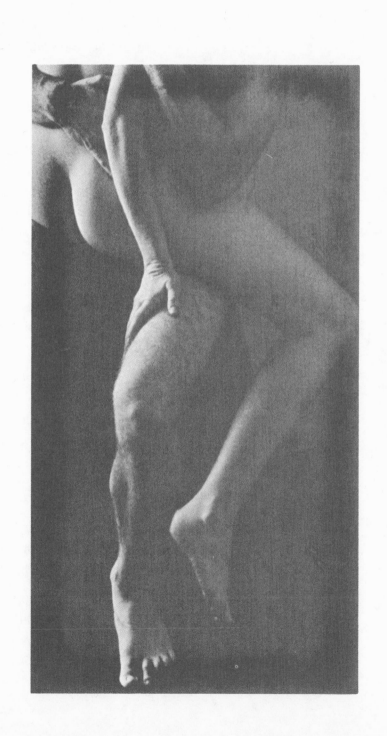

pincer around it. You can then move the clitoris back and forth, side to side, or in a circular motion. You can even twist it—gently—between the sides of your fingers.

4 – You can lay your hand over the hairy mound above your wife's genitals, so that one finger lies across the clitoris and over the lips of the vagina. You will then be able to gently massage the clitoris with the base of this finger. And the moisture that forms below will be pulled upward along your finger to the clitoris.

Regardless of which technique you use, if you do it well, the liquids will soon begin to form in sufficient amounts. You should make sure that you spread whatever moisture you can find over the clitoris in order to provide as smooth a stimulation as possible. (If not enough moisture develops, it is best that you provide the wetness yourself, either by using an artificial lubricant or by applying saliva to the area by finger or directly.)

At any rate, there won't be much moisture at the clitoris, itself, because most of it will have to be moved there from the vagina. Here, you should dip your finger into this area, just as you would into a honey pot!

Remember, the key to stimulation at this period is the clitoris, although, as your woman gains more experience—if she does not have this already—the nerves of other areas will become extremely sensitive and responsive. So, when you dip into that delightful honey pot below the clitoris, you may be tempted to shift your attention and caresses from the clitoris to the vagina. Nonetheless, you will be better off resisting this temptation. The clitoris is the key to bringing your woman to her greatest heights of excitement and you shouldn't abandon it just as your fondling of it becomes most effective.

It is very important that you always remember that soft, smooth stroking with the fingers works much better than hard, grating friction. The sure, silky touch is all-important. The unfortunate point about this is, however, that too many men have never learned the value of a satin-smooth caressing. Their touch is almost always too rough, sometimes feeling as harsh as sandpaper to a suffering woman! It's as if many men believe that being really masculine means being a rough Texas cowboy type. Just remember that in all the old cowboy movies, the rough Texas cowboy types were satisfied staying on the range with their horses—not hopping into bed with the womenfolk!

Anyway, once the moisture appears, there are many intriguing, pleasant, and different ways of stimulating the clitoris. Taking one finger, a man can stroke up one side and then down the other. The stroke can be continuous, circling and circling the now erect clitoris. Or, instead of stroking, he can tickle or vibrate, providing an infinite number of exciting sensations for the woman. He can place his full palm flat above the clitoris, allowing the tip to just brush against his palm as he rotates it around the area. He can stroke along the sides of the vulva with one finger, or he can stroke from back to front with the tips of all four fingers. Or the four fingers can dance lightly around the area, again and again lightly bumping into the clitoris—not hard enough to cause pain, but just enough to cause a series of little explosive sensations. Or, if it doesn't hurt the woman—some are too sensitive for this—the clitoris can be pressed inward with one finger, so that it pushes up against the soft skin around it. While maintaining light pressure against the clitoris, the finger can take up a slight rotating motion. But remember: some women are delighted by having this done to them, but other women cannot take this much sensation on the clitoris. Don't think that your woman is abnormal if one or another technique does not please her. Just experiment until you find out what you can and cannot do to your woman's clitoris.

A clitoris that is well-oiled, properly lubricated, responds very well to cross-way or length-way frictions at either tip or base, front to back or back to front. In other words, you can

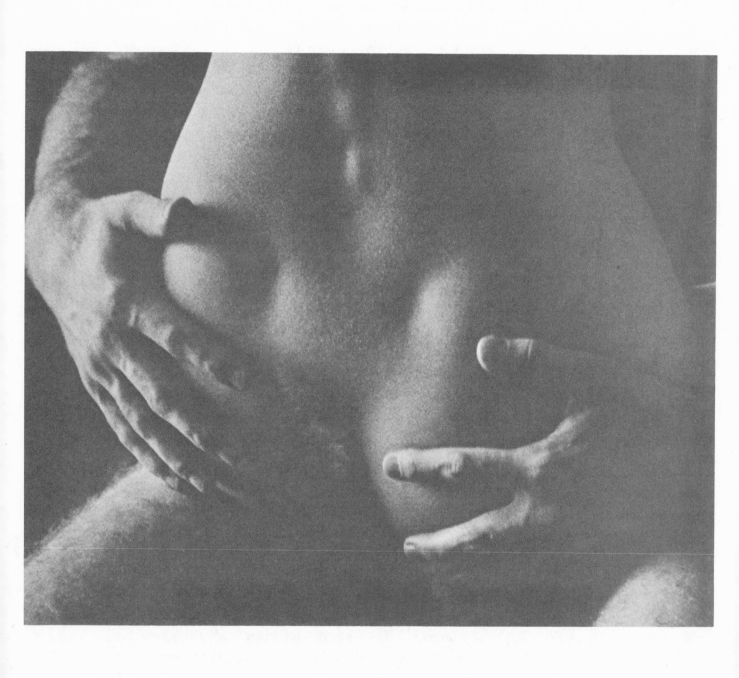

stimulate the clitoris in any direction at all. You can try stimulating the clitoris with the fleshy part of the finger, the side of the finger shaft, the back of your finger, or with the knuckle. There won't be any one best way of doing it, and you should vary your caresses from time to time. At the times when you are caressing the vagina, you can rub the base of the index finger and the knuckle, or the plump part of the thumb tip, across and along the clitoris. You can use your palm to rub the clitoris while you are caressing the vagina— this causes a more diffuse, subtler sensation than any finger causes, and is especially valuable if your woman is very sensitive to continued play with the clitoris. In other words, if your woman is easily irritated by too much caressing of the clitoris, the subtler sensations you can cause by using your palm may well be the answer. However you do it, with finger, knuckle, or palm, this caressing stimulation can be at any speed, in any direction, or in any possible way that takes your fancy. The main limitation on the number of ways you can stimulate the clitoris—besides the limits of your imagination—is the sensitivity of your partner. If her clitoris is one that can take a great deal of excitation without becoming irritated, then you are hardly limited at all. If her clitoris is very sensitive and easily irritated, then you must limit yourself somewhat more. And your experiments should be directed toward finding highly exciting, but still subtle, techniques. For instance, you might find it very rewarding to reach between her legs, past the vagina, to the buttocks, which you can stimulate with your palms, your fingers, and even your fingernails—while the soft skin of the underside of your forearm rubs back and forth, side to side, or in gentle circles, across the clitoris. Even with this technique, you will have to take care not to press your forearm too hard against the sensitive little organ. Of course, your partner will be in a position to control this pressure somewhat, in that she can grip your forearm between her thighs. And she can use her thighs to hold or release your forearm when she wants more or less pressure on her clitoris. (Your forearm will also be

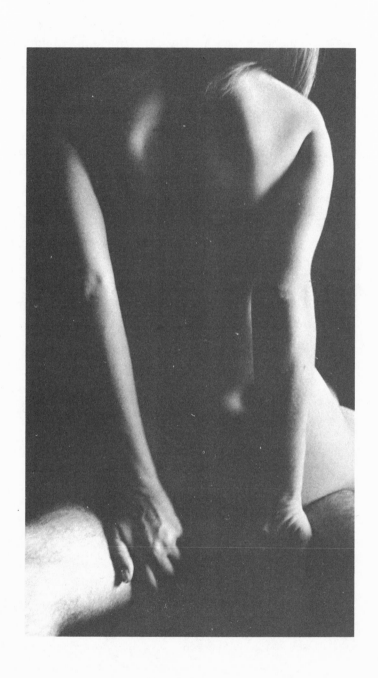

stimulating the lips of the vagina, while it stimulates the clitoris, and the titillation of the buttocks will also add to the excitement your partner gains while you do this.)

In using your hand directly on the clitoris, there are two things to be careful of: First, don't continue friction type caressing after the clitoris begins to get dry again without first lubricating it; a woman, like any piece of delicate machinery, needs to be well-oiled to run smoothly! And, second, don't use the fingernail; these very sensitive parts of the body will scratch easily—and a scratched clitoris can scratch your partner from the race to excitement for more than just one evening. (Although, if you are very careful, it usually would be perfectly all right to use the flat surface—not the edge—of your fingernail for stimulation.)

It is important to remember that when a woman has acquired a certain degree of experience, other areas of her genitals become increasingly sexually responsive. (Any sort of experience will have this effect of increasing the sensitivity of these areas. The young woman who has not often engaged in intercourse, but who has masturbated—or been masturbated —over an extended period of time, or who, before marriage, petted extensively without having intercourse often, may still have developed the sexual responsiveness of these other genital parts). The inner lips become very susceptible to stimulation. These can be caressed—given sufficient lubrication—with one finger stroking, or one can grasp the lip between the thumb and finger, caressing its length with a very gentle pressure. Or, try flicking it gently with your finger. Another method is to fold the index and middle fingers together, and catch one inner lip between them for a rolling, pressing caress which rubs one of the knuckles against the clitoris. A variation on this is to catch the other lip between the middle and third fingers in the same manner as the middle and index fingers have caught the first lip. In this fashion, each lip is being caressed, the clitoris is being stimulated by a knuckle, and the knuckle of your middle finger is subtly pressing into your partner's depths, stimulating the inner walls of her vagina and also drawing lubrication out from its source within her.

Always remember that these folds of tissue, the lips as well as the clitoris, must have moisture before they can be rubbed. For this end, you can rely on natural body secretions, artificial lubricants, or moisture from the mouth. And, throughout the time that you caress these parts, you must make sure that a sufficient level of lubrication remains to prevent friction irritation. The best way to assure that there is continuously enough lubrication is to maintain a continuously increasing level of excitement in your partner, uninterrupted by irritation or distraction. In most women, the genitals supply enough lubrication, steadily enough, to permit your caresses to be most enjoyable to the organs involved.

Inner-lip caressing not only gives you a way of stimulating your woman's passion—and enjoying yourself—but you can also use these caressing motions as a way of judging the extent and level of your woman's passion. It's sort of like taking your woman's sexual temperature (or, more precisely, her sexual temperature and humidity level), to learn accurately how far she has come along. Naturally, different women vary and the extent which the inner lips expand will vary to a great extent. However, the lips usually swell up so much that they stick out and push the outer lips aside. At the same time, the inner lips reflect their bloated, swollen condition by thickening into hard ridges instead of the softer folds they were before you started. Of course, this change in hardness will show you that your woman's passion is proceeding satisfactorily—similar to the way in which your own penis hardens with excitement and stands as tangible proof of the extent of your sexual excitement. (And, just as the erection of your penis is physical preparation—along with the natural secretion of lubricating fluids—for accepting your penis into her body. But, like anything else about sex, the things which prepare for the consummation and climax are not just of value as preparations. Much of the pleasure in sex—like the pleasure in going to a vacation spot—is in getting there!)

The man who considers the vaginal lips to be nothing more than gates through which his penis passes during intercourse, understands little about women or about sexual power. The lips are highly sensitive—especially, as we have noted, in women who have had some degree of sexual experience. Like the clitoris, stimulation here can bring your woman to the heights of ecstasy—and may even bring her to a climax! Try using the three large fingers of one hand on this area. Place your hand, palm away from the vagina, grasping the outer lips between the backs of your fingers. Your middle finger will then be stimulating the inner lips, its knuckles rubbing gently back and forth on these sensitive tissues. If you try this technique *after* the inner lips have swollen somewhat, the effect of bringing the outer lips back into place over the inner lips may be especially pleasing to your woman.

Try grasping the lips between your fingers with your palm pressed gently against her clitoris. This way, the tip of your middle finger can slowly, softly, inch its way deeper into the increasingly stimulated, and increasingly wet, vagina.

Try tickling the entire area, concentrating on the vaginal lips. Most women will respond to this tantalizing sensation. Take your time at it; allow your fingers to drift away from the vagina to tickle the inner thighs or the buttocks. (Some women will enjoy your casually including the anus and the area immediately surrounding it among the areas you tease gently with your fingertips on one of your excursions away from the vagina.) Then return to the lips for more tickling and teasing.

And don't neglect to use your penis in the pleasant business of stimulating the vaginal lips. There is no law that says you must thrust inside as soon as your penis approaches your wife's vagina—even if she expects this kind of rush job. Use the head of your penis as a tickler along the lips of the vagina. Move it up to gently nudge the clitoris. Then, return to the lips, taking your time before the actual penetration. Your penis will get a warmer welcome *inside* if it has lovingly tantalized on the *outside* first.

Another area that comes alive sexually after only a very few months of sexual experience is the back corner of the vaginal outlet. This, too, is a place for taking a woman's sexual temperature. This corner becomes extremely moist very early in the sex play preceding intercourse, so that a man can caress it and use it as a source of moisture at the same time. (This is a key approach in attaining full sexual power: use the excitement that has already been achieved to help you achieve even greater excitement of your woman.)

One form of stimulation is to use the side-to-side friction along the back of the vagina with the finger stuck in about one inch. Or, a man can use a rotary caressing motion in which a finger is inserted into the outlet and moved in a circular motion. Here is something else a man can do: he can grasp the muscle body just behind the vaginal opening with the fingers and rub these muscles between the thumb and fingers, jiggling them up and down and from side to side, even stretching them downwards or squeezing them. Even a mild amount of pain caused by such caresses will be enjoyed by many women.

After a while, when a woman has had about one year's experience (and, of course, this will vary greatly from one woman to another), the tube leading from the bladder to the outside becomes very sensitive. This lies in front of the vagina, and thus is between the inserted penis and the pelvic bone. The man can rub one or two fingers up along the front walls of the vagina and push it toward the woman's pubic bone, thus simulating the action of the penis in certain intercourse positions. The finger should then be used with an in and out motion that is quite firm and which, of course, duplicates the motions and the sensations caused by the penis during intercourse.

The entire female genital area is receptive to loving play. Subtle pressures on the outside—applied directly on the vaginal opening or from the area above the Mound of Venus—for instance, are felt deep inside. Stimulation of the whole area at once is especially exciting to most women. (Your wife may be among these—so try it!) Gently grasp the entire area in one hand, the heel of your hand resting on the Mound of Venus, applying a slight pressure, your palm gently pumping against the clitoris, your fingers exploring and teasing the lips and the back corner of the vagina.

Some men believe that they must stimulate their women according to a plan of progress that goes from general caresses to titillation of one little area to penetration—first by finger and then by penis. This belief is ridiculous! Sex isn't an assembly-line operation; you can switch back and forth in techniques and foreplay all you (or your woman) want. Pity the poor woman who always knows exactly what to expect, when, and for how long, every time her husband makes love to her!

And encourage your wife to experiment with different responses to what you do. When you grasp the entire vaginal region, for instance, there are any number of ways your wife can respond. She may want to just lie back, with her legs spread wide, allowing you complete freedom to caress her as you wish. Or she may allow her excitement to cause her to roll her hips as you play with her vagina.

Or she may clamp her legs together around your hand. This will limit your hand somewhat, but the clamping actions force the inner walls of the vagina together and add extra sensations to the play you are doing. As you explore, her leg muscles force the inner walls of the vagina together and apart, back and forth and sideways against each other, so that the stimulation caused by your hand on the outside is echoed by your woman's self-stimulation on the inside.

Use everything you have to please your woman. Your hand is versatile and your penis is satisfying, but your mouth, tongue, teeth, arm, and knee can also be used. As you stand or lie together, your knee, raised between your woman's slightly spread legs, can apply a gentle and very effective

91

pressure to her genital area. A very slight back and forth motion will increase the effectiveness. You can create this motion with your knee, but, in a standing position, it may be better to hold your knee steady and allow your woman to lower herself against it and move back and forth on your knee while you hold her against your body.

Almost all women are extremely excited by mouth-play on the vagina. And most men enjoy doing this. Experiment with various techniques. Your tongue can titillate the clitoris, the vaginal lips, or the inside of the vagina. Find out which your wife likes best—and there's only way to find out: try everything! Most women will also enjoy *gentle* biting of the clitoris, or gentle scraping by teeth, without nibbling, up and down the clitoris. Be careful, though! A little pain may be pleasant, but biting *too* hard can be extremely painful.

Your wife will probably derive most pleasure from your sucking her clitoris. Start gently, using light suction, while your tongue darts around the clitoris. Gradually increase the suction. Rotating your mouth on the area, or moving your head up and down, while using all the suction you can, will bring your woman to great heights of sensual pleasure. Most women can reach a climax this way—and be ready for intercourse immediately afterwards. The vagina—not having been penetrated before or during climax, except by the tongue or finger—will be especially sensitive to the penis.

Depending on the position you are in, you will be able to use one or both of your hands on various parts of your woman's body while your mouth is exciting her genitals. You may use your fingers to titllate her anus, to massage her buttocks, or to tease her inner thighs. Or you may reach up and caress her breasts or her belly. Or you may position yourself so that your woman can handle—or mouth—your genitals while you are mouthing hers. (Some women enjoy holding onto an erect penis with one hand while being caressed. Fondling or caressing the penis might be too distracting while being petted, but just holding on tightly may add, rather than distract from, the woman's pleasure while being petted.)

Stimulating the vagina itself is very useful. A simple in-and-out motion of one or two fingers, plunging as deep as possible and withdrawing almost completely, can be utilized to build the sexual ecstasy of the woman. The man can take his woman's sexual temperature while exploring within her vagina, noting the dampness and the swollen softness of the vaginal walls. These caresses can also be used to provide the woman with more orgasms than the man can normally provide just with his penis.

There are any number of ways you can use your fingers inside your woman's vagina to stimulate her sexual excitement. One finger, the index or middle finger, or both, can be inserted stiffly (keeping the two fingers together when two are used). This imitation of the penis can be used in an in-and-out motion, pressing hard on one wall of the vagina. Or two fingers (or more) can be spread out within the vagina to spread it, applying exaggerated pressure on several points along the inner walls. But there is no reason to keep the finger or fingers stiff the whole while. Unlike a penis, a finger can bend and twist in every direction, playing along the walls. A rotating motion, a side-to-side motion, or a combination of motions can be used as well as the basic in-and-out motion. Where more than one finger is inserted, it is also possible to simply hold them in place, not moving in or out, or side to side, but subtly spreading them in a pulsating rhythm. Don't move the fingers far apart or fast. Just use a slow, subtle, pulsing rhythm. Some women will respond wildly to this technique.

Another thing you might try usually is very effective, but you may have to overcome inhibitions (yours or hers) in order to really enjoy this. First, insert the index finger into the vagina, moving it around to get it very wet. Then remove it and insert the thumb in its place. With the thumb planted deeply in the vagina, gently introduce your wet index finger into your woman's anus. You must go slowly and be very gentle. (A harsh or fast motion may cause her to involuntarily

95

contract muscles that will reject your finger and cause her pain —and ruin her excitement.) When the index finger has finally slipped inside, you will be in a position to grasp the vaginal wall between your thumb and finger and use a gentle massage of that wall that is simply not possible in any other way. Many women get extreme pleasure out of this technique; try it on your woman if she is willing.

Stimulating the Male Genitals

When your woman first begins to caress your genitals, she should usually begin with the scrotum and the top of the penis. The usual method is to very lightly stroke the back of the scrotum, beginning an inch or two behind the sac and then working her way downwards. Before moving away from this sensitive area behind the testicals, she might try applying pressure—not too hard—upward with two or three fingers.

Your woman should let the scrotum lie gently on the flat of her fingers and hands, and then make use of a number of common techniques of caressing. She can bounce the testicles about among her fingers, ever so gently scratching and rubbing the back of the scrotum with the fingernails and fingertips. If she wishes, she could also use her thumb at the front or even try rolling the loose folds of skin between her thumb and fingers. She can either move on from here to the penis or she could keep playing with the testicles with one hand while she caresses the penis with her other hand.

Of course, the same thing must be said about her playing with your genitals as was said about your playing with hers. There is no reason for her to follow a prepared routine. A hand that has moved from testicles to penis can always drift back to the testicles. One time, your woman may decide to neglect the scrotum entirely, to concentrate her loving caresses on your penis. Another time, she might linger over caressing the scrotum, barely touching your penis at all. Sometimes, she might want to absent-mindedly play with your genitals while you caress hers. Another time, she might throw all her energies into exciting you—and delighting herself—by playing with your genitals.

96

She can stroke the penis along the top, from the base to the tip, or, if she wants, she can try flickering the top of the penis with her finger, all the while scratching and pinching it. If she does this, you will feel intense excitement, just as you will if she uses a gentle and quivering patting with her fingers at the top of the penis.

If your woman doesn't do it on her own, get her to try pinching the scrotal area very gently, and you will find this most exciting and stimulating. (Perhaps *too* stimulating, so this should be reserved for the final moments before climax.)

Another widely used method is for your woman to clutch the penis and barely hold it in her hands. Also, of course, she can move her hand up and down the shaft, but if she does this she should make sure that she does it very carefully, so that she doesn't trigger you off prematurely.

Should you be very tired or overly burdened with worry, and because of this find it difficult to give rise to a hard and complete erection, your partner can take the shaft of your penis in one hand and the head of your penis in her other hand, and then gently move her hands around in opposite directions—just as if she were "wringing" the organ. Such a method can bring almost any man's penis to a rock-hard erection almost at once. When this method is applied to an already excited penis, it can still cause enormous pleasure. This technique is known as the "Sexual Explosion."

Your woman can try caressing or scratching, even pinching, along the area of the urinary tube at the bottom of the penis. She can push the tips of two or three of her fingers hard into this area. This method, too, is most stimulating and should be used with care.

Using one hand only, your woman can try gripping around the base of the penis head with her fingernails, vibrating them rapidly. If she does this while using the fingers of her other hand to press upward in the sensitive area behind your scrotum, she will have to be very careful or she'll trigger your climax prematurely.

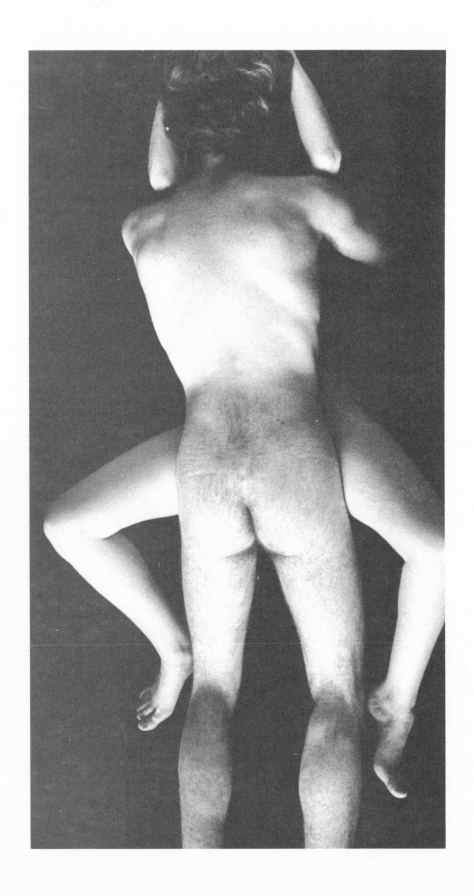

If your penis is somewhat wet, your woman can massage the wet head of your penis with the flat of her thumb. Done gently, this is extremely pleasant, but is safe, in that it is unlikely to cause a premature climax.

Another technique which your woman may enjoying trying is similar to rolling strips of dough. She places your penis between her open hands, rolling it from side to side. This is useful in hardening an incomplete erection, but it can also be used whenever your woman feels like "rolling dough."

Of course, you should let your partner use her imagination and try whatever she feels like trying. If she enjoys doing it— and you enjoy having it done to you—then it's right.

For instance, not all men will enjoy this technique: the woman gets a good grip on the penis and pulls—hard. While not all men enjoy this, you may be among those who do. If so, let her do it—most women really enjoy this.

Some women enjoy using a much subtler approach, and most men enjoy this, too. Your woman teases your thighs or lower belly, brushing her wrist or forearm "accidentally" against your scrotum and penis. As a part of a long, leisurely love session, this can be especially valuable.

Like women, men also can enjoy love-play involving the anus. Unfortunately, many men are very inhibited about this, thinking that there is something "queer" about this. Nonsense! When you are making love with your woman, anything that works is worth trying—and it's worth trying anything that might work. Some Oriental prostitutes regularly make use of the sensitivity of their clients' anuses. During intercourse, they quietly insert a knotted cord into the man's anus—without his noticing. At the climax, the prostitute quickly pulls the cord out, adding an extra sensation to that of the orgasm. This device is not really appropriate for most love-making, but the point is that the sensitivity of a man's anus can play as much of a part in sex as the sensitivity a woman has there. For instance, a quick thrust into the man's anus as he has his orgasm

101

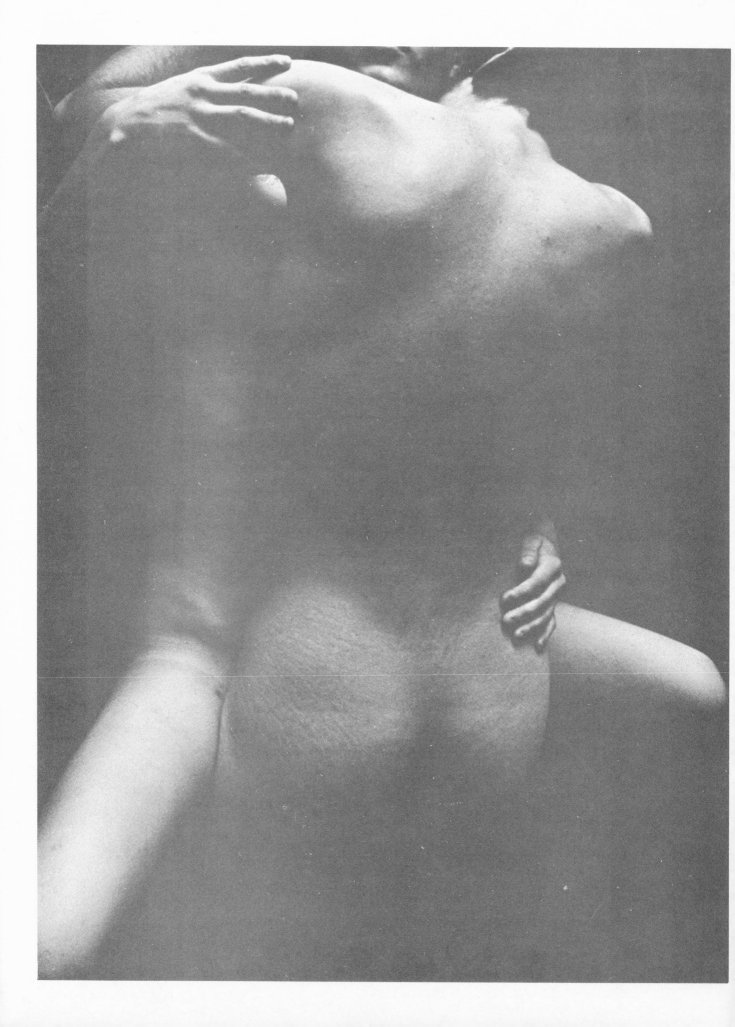

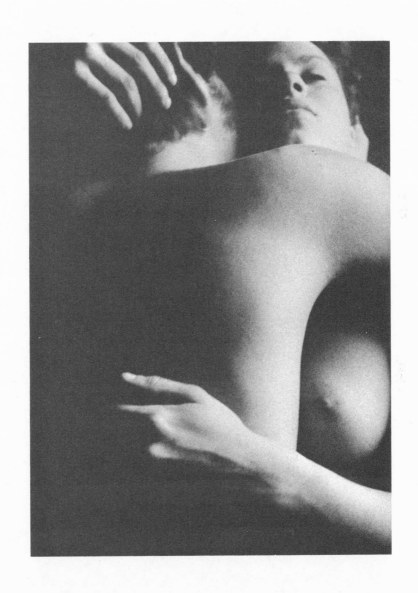

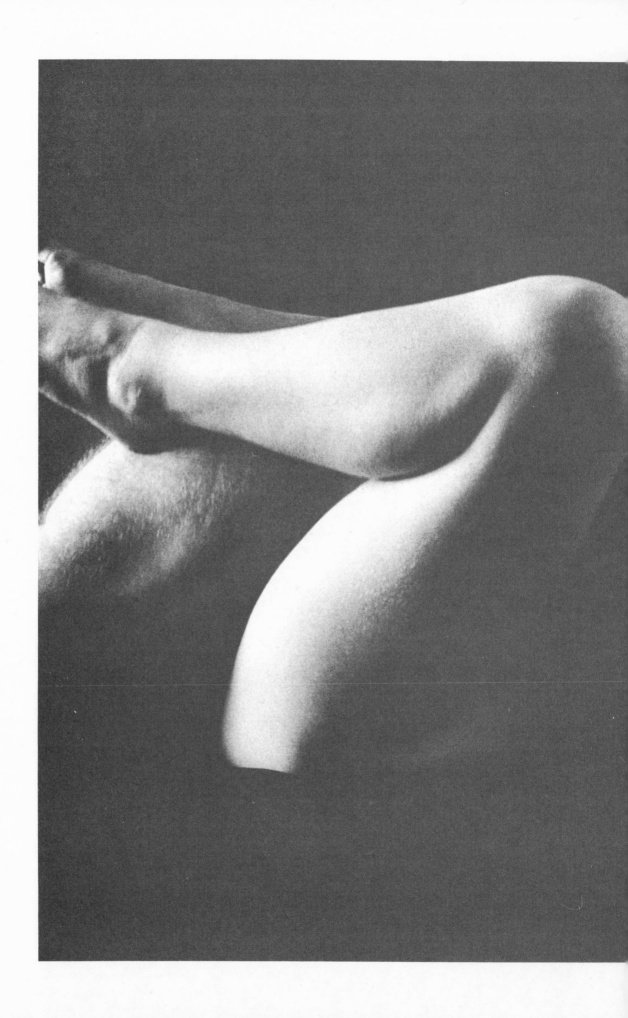

can add to his pleasure—and cause you to drive deeper into your woman at that moment. It may take some convincing to get your woman to try this—but that may be the case with a lot of things you may want to try (or have her try) in your sexual adventures.

An essential part of the caressing of the male genital area is with your woman's mouth. This type of caressing is very much valued by any man, and any woman who even tries to neglect this form of mouth-play is neglecting an important part of her duty as a fully cooperative partner. Besides, any woman who is a real woman will get pleasure by giving pleasure in this fashion—and, at least once in a while, will absolutely crave bringing you to completion this way.

Your woman should take your penis into her mouth, gently sucking in and out, in and out. She should draw the penis as far into her mouth as she can manage. The first few times she tries this, she may gag and have difficulty getting much of your penis into her mouth. Assure her that you're not insulted by her gagging (some women are embarrassed by gagging) and let her try again. After a few times, she should be able to get as much in as her mouth can physically hold. (Of course, if you should happen to have an extra large penis, the woman will only be able to suck and caress the head and very little of the shaft. This shouldn't make much difference to you, though) With this type of caressing and sucking, it's the head of the penis that really matters, of course. Therefore, she should try moving her lips around the lower edge of the head, caressing the sensitive nerves. Then, she should bring her teeth into play, gently biting into the head and at the neck of the head—again, where the sensitive nerves can be stimulated. Some women will be afraid to use their teeth on the penis; it is up to you to show your woman what she can and cannot do. You have to let her know that the slight pain her teeth cause you actually feels good to you. But, of course, you have to let her know if the pain passes beyond the pleasure point.

106

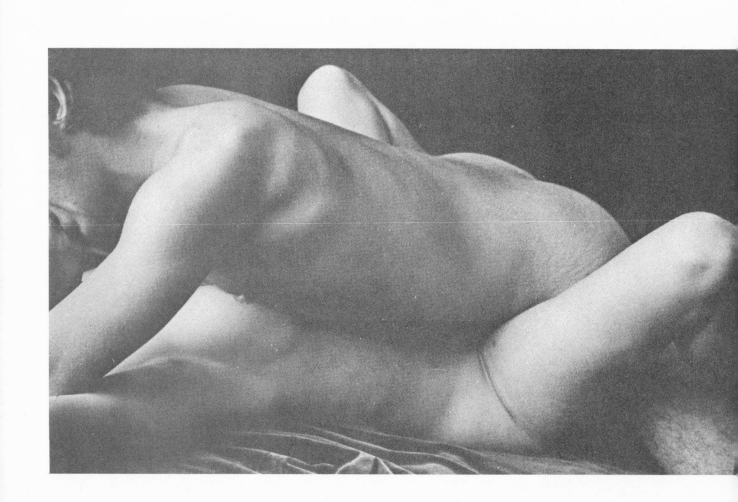

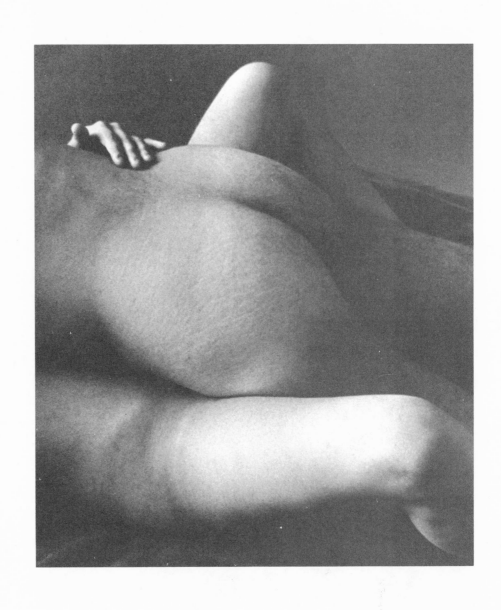

She should also blow continuously and vigorously while her mouth is on your penis head or on the shaft. And her tongue should be made full use of, especially as its rough surface makes it especially suitable for this kind of work. Even before putting your penis into her mouth, she can use her tongue all over the head and shaft of your penis, tickling the opening in the head, tracing around the base of the penis head, "washing" the head, or tracing the tube up and down the underside of your penis. While your penis is in her mouth, she should continue to use her tongue, darting around the head while she is sucking, blowing, or biting.

Fitting a large object like a penis into the mouth and then sucking or blowing is tiring, no matter how much your woman enjoys doing it. For this reason, your woman will be able to caress your penis with her mouth for a long period only if she uses various techniques that give her mouth muscles a chance to rest.

For instance, putting the penis in, head first, is not the only way to get the mouth around part of the penis. Your woman can also try grasping the length of the shaft, with the underside of the penis in her mouth, lengthwise. In this type of caress, the head of the penis isn't in the mouth at all. Your woman should suck and blow on the underside, being sure to use her tongue in rapid licking motions.

Also, your woman can pucker her lips against the head of the penis without putting more than the very tip of it in her mouth, using her tongue and front teeth to excite the tip.

Or she can put her lips against the very base of the penis, at the top of the scrotum, vibrating her lips rapidly by humming.

All in all, it usually takes very little motion of the teeth, tongue, lips, and blowing motions on the head of the penis to bring a man to the point of climax in a very short time. For this reason, therefore, it should be obvious that great care should be used with this technique.

As we mentioned before, the fingers and fingernails are almost as effective on the head of the penis as the mouth is. Again, it takes very little caressing, tickling, or gentle pinching to bring about immediate action. A quick but very, very gentle scratch across the nerve area at the neck of the penis has often been compared to pulling the trigger of a loaded pistol.

Thus, to reemphasize this point: because a man always tends to come to climax much faster than a woman, the female sex partner should take care and use restraint in caressing the man's genitals. Remember—it only takes one or two motions at the wrong time and wrong place to destroy perfect harmony. It is your job to teach your woman perfect timing. And teach her you must. Any woman who has not been taught properly or is too ignorant or sexually backward ever to grasp the techniques of correct timing—such a woman is next to useless sexually and has no place in your bed.

On the other hand, there may well be occasions in an extended relationship when the woman *wants* to complete the love-play with her hands, mouth, or both.

Of course, it has to be remembered that there is no law against more than one orgasm per day for either a man or a woman. Your sex play isn't over when your woman reaches climax, and it doesn't have to be over if you get there first. And a woman who wants more after her man has reached a climax should know the techniques of bringing back to life what has passed. After a short time allowed for you to get your breath, your woman should be able to arouse you again by using her hands and mouth. If the penis is no longer erect at all, your woman may be able to grasp it almost entirely in her mouth, gently massaging it with her tongue until it becomes erect again.

After an orgasm, the penis is usually very sensitive and can be irritated easily, so your woman will have to be very, very gentle. But she should still be able to make it ready again. Starting off by simply kissing your scrotum and penis, she might then hold the scrotum in one hand while carefully stimulating the penis with her fingers, tongue and mouth. It is usually best to warn her not to use her teeth at this time—but you are the best judge of this and you must guide her along.

113

3

Scaling New Heights

SUCCESSFUL sex must finish with a wild, ecstatic ending. Ideally, the climax should be the ultimate—all that could be imagined and much more than either partner expected. Here are some ways in which this might be achieved.

The Final Caresses

Pain and pleasure often go together. The sexual climax comes about through stimulation of nerve endings, and the intense pleasure responses here are similar to pain responses. Thus, near the sexual climax, there really isn't much difference between pain and pleasure; it is the intensity of stimulation that is most important. Caresses which cause both pain and pleasure in sexually sensitive areas that are already highly excited will heighten one's climax more than gentler caresses that cause less intense sensations, not including pain. The spots on which to concentrate one's attentions and caresses will vary from individual to individual. And the spots where pain and pleasure are most effectively combined—and the amount of pain that is effective—will also depend on the particular tastes and sensitivities of the person involved. Nevertheless, it is possible to point out a few areas which are usually worth caressing and stimulating at this point of love-play.

Pinch and clutch at the buttocks, thighs, and belly. This will often prove very effective and stimulating. Dig your fingers into the flesh, and grasp it with all the strength in your fingers. During the final moments, little touches and pluckings of the flesh have little effectiveness. The time is past in which to

117

tease the skin. Teasing will only annoy now, so dig right in! Be vigorous, firm, and often rough. The time for gentleness was at the beginning stages of sex play; don't be subtle, now! Slap the lower back and buttocks quite hard. There is no danger of injury; the sting of a well placed and well delivered slap is often intense, though brief, and the resulting warmth of the slap can be very exciting to many people. (Stretching your woman naked over your naked lap is an excellent way to deliver such a slap, but, of course, it isn't the only way, and it can be delivered during intercourse in some positions.) Remember, the woman may protest strongly the first time you use this "treatment," and she may complain that you are being too rough—but it is far better to be a little too vigorous during the final moments than to be a little too gentle, tender, and dull. Of course, a man—because he has the strength—must use a certain degree of restraint when he handles his woman during intercourse. After all, extremes in this field eventually lead to perversion—and an end to the fullest satisfactions of sex. (In fact, sexually unbalanced men will, in rare cases, lose control of themselves during these moments of ecstasy and will brutally injure and sometimes even kill their women. Of course, it wasn't intentional; they merely lost control of themselves—but this hardly mattered to the victims of their uncontrolled passions.) Within reasonable limits, pain is a useful and completely legitimate tool to stimulate a woman—and, for that matter, it is just as useful and just as legitimate a tool for a woman to use to stimulate her man.

While your woman might not always like the immediate shock of pain, from a slap or a pinch or a bite, she will reap the benefits enormously moments later when she feels the pleasurable sensations creeping and flowing over her.

Pinching the scrotum brings many men toward ecstasy and can make the final moment of intercourse the very summit of satisfaction. There are enough techniques for "triggering the loaded pistol" that a woman can almost always bring her man to climax just when she wants. Women who want to feel the orgasm of their man at the moment of their own climax should feel free to use these passion-heightening devices.

Pinching the scrotum is often the easiest and best device, but there are any number of others. Jabbing the anus is one, jabbing behind the scrotum is another, and a quick jab of the tongue into one ear is often yet another device. In some positions, the woman can drive a hand between her lower belly and her man's groin, and can grab the base of the penis, the rest of which is deep within her. A good squeeze here can have a "trigger" effect. Someimes, grabbing the man's buttocks and pulling them tightly toward the woman's body—forcing the penis to its full depth—will work, but this is less dependable (for most men) than some of the other devices already described. Of course, men vary, and the woman should experiment to find the "trigger" she can count on most dependably.

Biting the neck, shoulders, and chest can often prove very stimulating. Never forget to use both the teeth and the tongue and lips. While the teeth provoke pain, the lips and tongue also caress. Thus you provide your woman with the intriguing sensation of experiencing pain while simultaneously feeling the caressing touch of your lips and tongue. On the shoulder, you can really take a good hard bite, so that it almost seems that you are going right through to the bone. On the neck, you'll have to be more careful, and you can rely more on a sucking pressure that raises the blood vessels to the surface than on actually biting down. The chest has both tougher and more sensitive spots; only on the nipple itself must you really use much restraint.

The Use of Ice   Stimulating the same pain nerves that we have just been talking about can also be accomplished by freezing the skin. Before intercourse, your woman should gather together a bowl of ice wrapped in a piece of cloth. She should keep this near the bed, within easy reach. Suppose that you have begun your sex play (completely naked, of course) in any face-to-face position, with you on top. When you begin your final climb toward climax, your woman should pick up a handful of the ice and shove it against your crotch, holding it there until you have finished. Or, if your woman is on top of you, you can perform the same act.

119

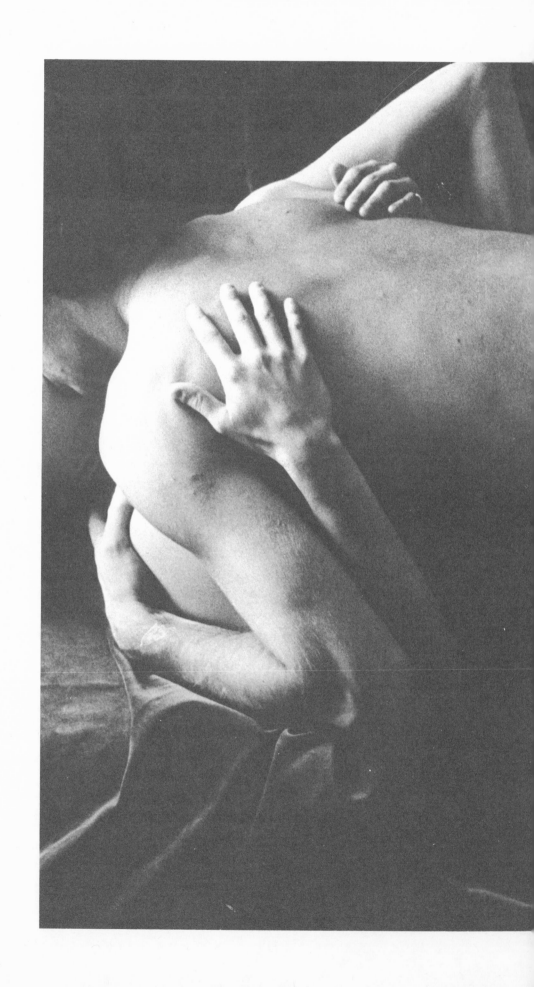

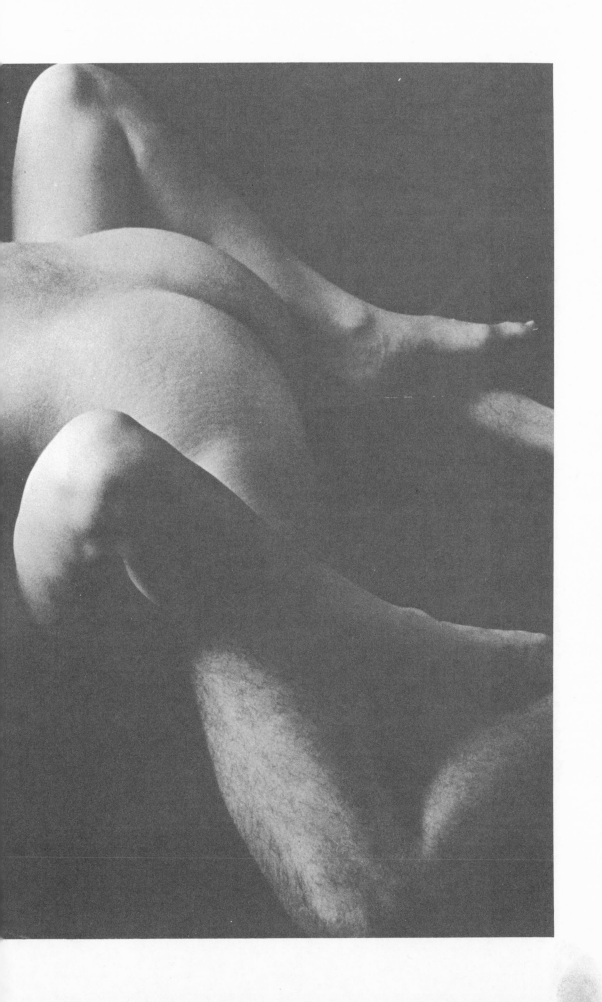

Now, you may find it somewhat uncomfortable for one or both of you to have ice cold water running all over your bodies, so there is an alternate way of doing this. The one who is using the ice can simply keep his (or her) hand on several pieces of ice in the bowl beside the bed, until the hand is cold. Then, use the frigid hand to stimulate the crotch.

During the lifetime of Porfirio Rubirosa, the semiprofessional Latin Lover, there were rumors that he used an ice bucket by the side of his bed to prolong sex. The rumors are probably false, but there is no doubt that ice can be used to add new and intense sensations to intercourse. Some people may think it too artificial a device, but remember the Golden Rule of dynamic sex: Do whatever works.

Pressure on the Urinary Passage Another useful technique is for your woman to press her bunched fingertips firmly into your flesh just behind your scrotum in a rather sharp jab right as you approach your climax. Your ejaculation originates in this area, and the pressure will send you into a soaring orgasm.

Women, too, as we have noted earlier, build up intensive sexual sensitivity in the urinary passage. Thus, you can delight your woman by exciting this sensitivity. You can press these organs—which you would not otherwise touch—into the range of the penis. You can do this by putting one hand against your woman's lower belly, just above the pubic bone, and press down quite firmly toward the pelvis—pushing her abdominal wall down toward the inner end of her organ.

Remember, it is an added touch like this that is the real content of sexual power. This is the sort of thing that adds the extra sensations that make the difference between mediocre sex play and full-fledged fireworks.

The Rocking Motions The rocking and rolling motions at an earlier stage of intercourse can still be very effective at the climax if the couple uses a faster rhythm. The main muscles to be used are those of the buttocks—the belly or the spine—and the

123

body action rolls the genital area in a back to front arc. The woman should keep at least one hand on the man's hips so that she is able to keep in rhythm with him. In a way, it is very much like keeping in time with the music!

These same rocking and rolling motions can be used in yet another way at the climax. Instead of combining these motions with a faster rhythm, the couple can use the rocking and rolling while maintaining the slower rhythm of the earlier stage. It often feels natural to speed up as the climax approaches. But it may sometimes be especially pleasurable to restrain yourself from speeding up as orgasm approaches. Even as your entire body tenses on the brink, hold your movements to the slow, sensual rhythm you had been using all along. The waves of orgasm can then roll in gently in a slow, overwhelming tide. Your woman may be surprised (and very pleased) by this change of pace—and by the size of the orgasm that can be achieved in this manner.

Oral-Genital Stimulation (The Panther's Kiss)

Here is a method of stimulation and love-play that is practiced by hundreds of millions of couples and, yet, for some bizarre reason, is still regarded by many as being not quite respectable. This is ridiculous, of course, and it is a shame that people deny themselves the value and pleasures of oral-genital stimulation just because, in some back alley of our culture, they heard that this was "wrong."

As a method of love-play, oral-genital kissing is essential. It is only abnormal when it is practiced obsessively, as a substitute for normal sexual union through intercourse. But this, however, does not come within the area under discussion in this book, which is only concerned with the normal practice of "normal" sex practices. (Of course, what is abnormal about obsessive oral-genital sexuality is not the oral-genital relationship, but is the obsession. And obsessive stamp collecting, obsessive drinking of malted milks, or obsessive anything is just as abnormal as obsessive use of oral-genital relations as a sole means of having sexual relations.)

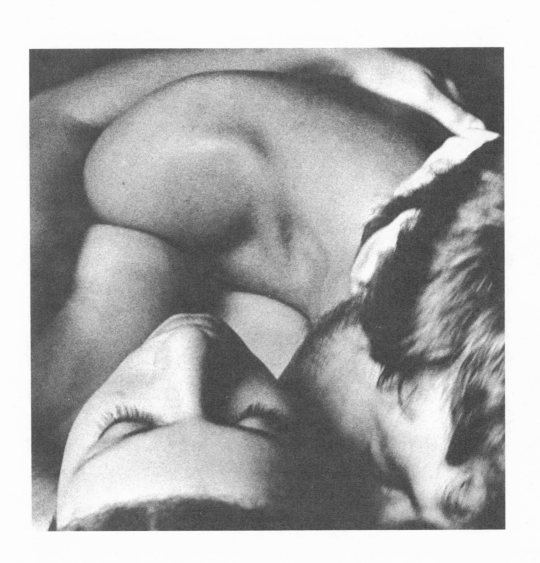

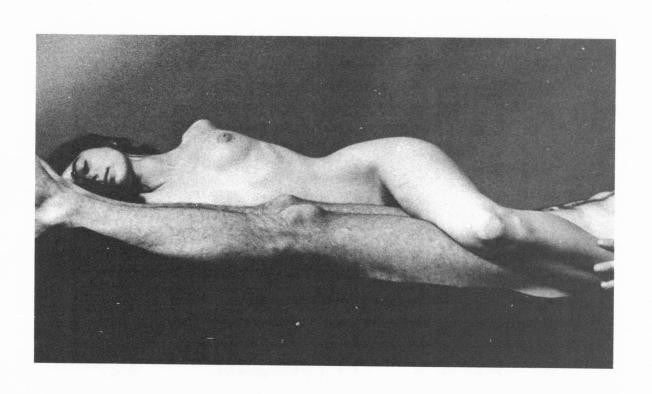

Now, there are two sorts of oral-genital relations: one-way and two-way. One partner can relax while the other performs oral caresses. Or, it can be a mutual, or two-way method of sexual stimulation—in other words, your two bodies are in opposite directions while each of you perform oral stimulation on the other's genitals.

First, let's consider the positions in which you can perform cunnilingus (oral caresses) on your woman

She can lie on her back with her knees up and thighs stretched apart—the conventional position for intercourse. In this position, her genital area is fully exposed to you—to your vision, to your explorations by hand, to your penis, and to your mouth. If you approach her from below, you can place your mouth on her clitoris or vagina and have your hands completely free to reach her belly or breasts, so that you can stimulate these while caressing her genitals with your mouth. While your mouth is on her vaginal opening, you will be able to tease her clitoris with your nose.

If your woman wants, she can lower her legs slightly and rest her thighs on your shoulders. Or, if you want, she can lower her legs further and grasp your head between her thighs while you mouth her clitoris.

Your wife can lie on her side, so that you are lying on your side in the opposite direction, but facing her. In this position, you can rest your head on her thigh while making love to her with your mouth. This position is usually less comfortable than the one described above.

It is also possible for you to lie flat on your back with your wife on her knees above you—so that you can look straight up the front of her body at her breasts. (You may want a pillow under your head.) From this position, you can caress your woman's vaginal area with your hands and mouth. The only real advantage of trying this position is that it is a change of pace, if you need one.

127

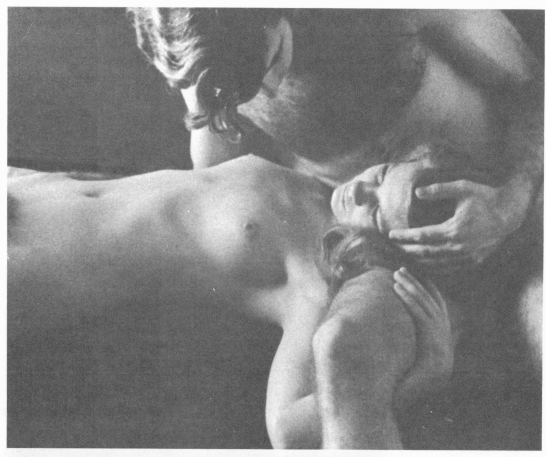

There are several positions in which your woman can perform fellatio (oral caresses) on you.

You can lie on your back and your woman can approach your penis from several different directions. She can get between your legs—this is just like the position described above for cunnilingus, with the partners reversed. Or she can lie at right angles to you or sit at your side or lie in the opposite direction from you, with her body sprawled across your abdomen and shoulder in such a way that one of your hands can caress her genitals.

You and your woman can use the side-to-side position described above for cunnilingus.

You can stand, with your woman kneeling before you, her hands reaching around to your buttocks while she sucks on your penis. This position stresses the dominant role of the man. It is a good position to use while showering together.

Should the genital kissing be mutual—that is, both doing it at the same time—several of the above positions can be used.

The position in which the woman lies flat on her back with her knees up against her body and her thighs spread can be used: here you mount her facing in the opposite direction, with your face over her vaginal area and your penis hanging above her mouth. This is a comfortable position, in which your woman's hands are free to take part in caressing your genitals or your buttocks. The only problem that sometimes appears in this position is that the man may get excited into motion by the fellatio and drive his penis hard into the back of the woman's throat. This can be very painful to the woman, whose head is almost literally pinned to the bed by the penis in her mouth.

Reversing position solves this problem. Here, the man lies on his back and the woman is on top. This way, the woman is freer to move her head on and around the penis, even though her hands are less free. The man's hands are now free to reach the breasts and caress them, or to caress the belly or buttocks, or to titillate the anus. A pillow under your head may be very helpful in giving you access to the vagina without your woman having to lower her weight onto your face. Many couples find this position most comfortable.

The side-to-side position is very comfortable, also. Each of you can use the other's thigh as a pillow and the love-play can be carried out leisurely. Each of you also has at least one hand free to caress the other partner during the mouth-play.

It is important that you find a mutually comfortable position, so that neither of you feels any particular hurry in concluding this stimulation. And there is no reason why one of you can't rest for a while in the course of this, allowing the other partner to do all the caressing for a while. If your woman is on top, she can lower her body onto you, lie her head on your thigh (still facing your penis), and rest for a few moments, savoring the delights of your caresses of her clitoris and vagina. If you are on top, she can simply lie back, letting your penis dangle across the side of her face, and rest. In the side-to-side position, it is also easy to rest up a bit. And you can take a break in any of these positions, resting and concentrating on the exciting sensations she is causing with her mouth on your genitals.

Whichever position you choose, you should make a place for oral-genital relations in your sex play. Don't let foolish inhibitions keep you and your woman from this very intimate and very delightful experience.

4

Building
Feminine
Passion

BUILDING your woman's passion is like building a fire. It takes care and preparation. After all, when you build a fire, you make the initial preparations of putting the wood together, carefully done so that you are sure of igniting a flame that will build into a blazing fire. Then, you strike the match, making sure that the flame has caught onto the fuel wood, and then you slowly nurse it along until the flame has grown and it has become a mighty—and mighty hot—fire. So it is with a woman. Again, when lighting the fire, you follow a certain pattern—a pattern that is dictated by the very nature of the fuel and placement of the potential fire. First, you ignite some paper or small twigs. You don't try to light a heavy log with a simple match. Naturally, it just wouldn't work. So it is that you don't try to build a woman's fervor by beginning at once with the violent actions that will occur near the climax. The same actions that will please her so much when she is ready for them could very easily repel, disgust, hurt, or cool her at too early a stage of the sex play. Instead, you begin at the beginning, with gentle stroking and caressing and—most important, soothing and gentle and beguiling words. You are working on the tinder of the sexual fire—you must use a simple match; keep your blow torch out of sight.

And, as with a fire, you have to be ready to add more and more fuel, larger and larger logs, when they are needed, so that the fire keeps growing, rather than cooling off before the campfire cooking is done.

135

You must also be careful to shield the fire from the elements that might douse the fire before it becomes really hot and big. In building your woman's sexual fire, you must guard her from the sexual elements that might douse her fire: pain, fear, clumsiness, distraction, anxiety, boredom, violent or gross actions, too much speed—all of which can cool a woman at the early stages of love-play.

And remember: neither of you can do any cooking until your woman's sexual fire is flaming strongly.

Warm Baths   You and your woman will find that soaking yourselves in a tub of hot water before sexual intercourse relaxes the muscles and spreads a hazy warmth throughout the body—and prepares the body wonderfully for tender stimulation.

Fill the tub with water as hot as you can comfortably stand—so hot that your skin positively tingles and you feel that a hundred thousand needles are sticking into you. Then, pour in a good dose of coconut oil and lie down in the water so that it is up to your neck. You will find that after emerging from the hot water, and after vigorously rubbing yourself down with a towel, your skin is warm and prickly and you are more than ready for what lies ahead. Remember to make sure that your woman also takes the same kind of bath. After all, you want her body ready to receive your caresses —with her skin and nerve endings keyed to teasing stimulation.

Sleep   Nobody can enjoy satisfactory sex if they are tired and feeling worn out. This is true of men, but it is even more true of women. A man who is too tired may not be able to perform at all, but if he can perform, he can get pleasure out of it. (Although a tired man is not likely to be a vigorous and active lover.) But a woman who is run down or fatigued may allow herself to be made love to, but she won't be able to get much pleasure out of it and she isn't going to be a responsive partner. Unfortunately, too many men think of women as being nothing more than objects in bed and never

136

know the wonderful pleasures of making love *together* with their partners. For these men, a tired wife can be no worse than a wife who isn't tired—but these men get little from their sex lives, anyway. (And the poor women they're married to . . . !)

If your wife has been working too hard in the fields or factory, in an office or store, or even at home—or wherever she spends her day—it is unrealistic to expect her to enjoy sexual union with vigor and earnestness. Too often, she will display all the responsiveness of a limp sack, and the excitability of a dead mackerel. Remember: don't overwork your wife if you want her to be a real woman in bed. Whatever little satisfaction you get by knowing she is bringing in a little money, you will more than lose in your sexual relationship. Naturally, different women have different levels of strength and robustness. If your wife has all the stamina of an elephant—but can still be a pussycat in your bed—then your problems in this regard may be nonexistent. In fact, it may be that you are the one in your marriage who needs to build up—or conserve—strength and stamina!

Don't overlook this point. If you are knocking yourself out at work every day and moonlighting on a second job or grabbing all the overtime you can get, you may be earning that extra money at the expense of your sexual happiness and your wife's sexual satisfaction. Remember: any woman who is a real woman would rather have a little less money and a little more—and better—loving. After all, a fur coat can keep a woman warm, but it takes a man to get her hot!

Just as important, don't bring worries about your work into bed with you. You may say that that is easier said than done, but it must be done! There are thousands of men who ruin their sex lives by worrying about work in bed—and then ruin their careers by being distracted about sex or sexually frustrated when they should be working. It's a vicious circle and the place to end it is in bed. Put aside your troubles and let yourself go. You may find that a more exciting sex life with

137

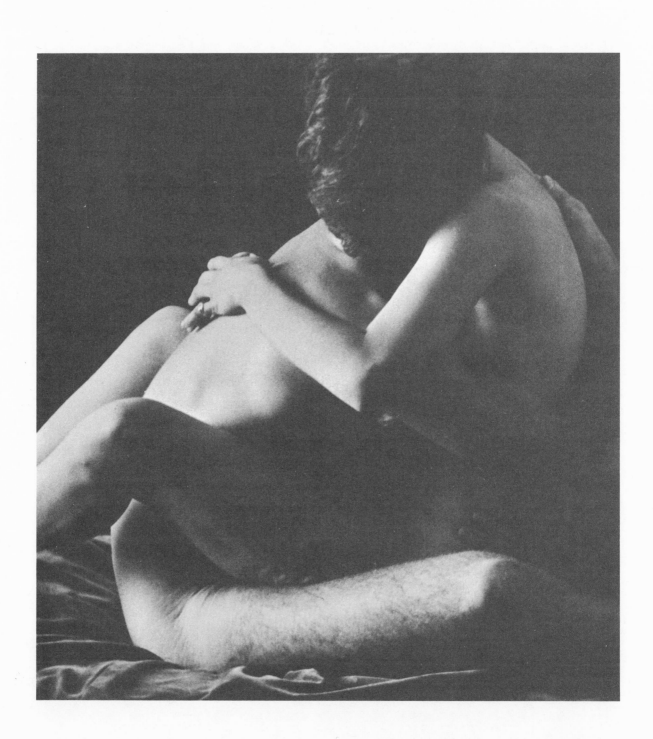

your wife will better equip you to devote your energies to dealing with your job problems.

If fatigue is a basic problem in your sexual relationship with your wife, you simply must solve it if you are ever to have fully satisfactory sex. Fortunately, most people should be able to solve this problem if they really try.

For one thing, there is no law that sex has to be a bedtime event. The morning, when both of you are rested after a night's sleep, may be a better time for many couples. Or you might try taking a nap as soon as you get home from work. In this way, you will be somewhat rested when it becomes time to go to bed. Try it: take a nap after work, eat dinner somewhat later than you usually do, and relax a bit after dinner. By bedtime, you should be ready to do your best and enjoy it the most.

On the weekends—or on any days off—you might try having sex during the afternoon. After all, it should be more fun than mowing the lawn or watching a ball game on TV!

Sexual
Control
It is essential in any sexual partnership that both parties remember that the extent of the man's penetration and the woman's sexual motions are limited by the man's tendency toward a fast climax. In the most successful sexual encounter, the too-quick male orgasm must be avoided. All the other rules of the game follow from this basic law. (It is not normally a problem, in any sexual encounter, to control or delay the female orgasm, in that the woman is normally slower to climax and also in that a female climax does not have the same disruptive effect on the mechanics of intercourse that a male climax usually has. In other words, after an orgasm, she's still there, but he isn't!) With this in mind, two points should be emphasized:

> 1 — Successful sex depends on relaxation. Because
> muscular tension, and with it, nervous energy,
> is a basic part of sex, you must learn to control

140

muscular tension and relaxation in a very short period. This is not as easy as it may seem, and it takes practice, but the efforts you make in this area will be well rewarded. Of course, some people find this easier than others and some people find this extremely difficult. Try this and work at it:

Lie down on a bed or on a carpeted floor, with all your clothes off, in a partially darkened room. Lie on your back with your arms at your sides, relax completely, and let your mind float. Dismiss worries and irritations from your mind and let all tension ease from your body.

Many people think that physical relaxation and mental relaxation are two different things entirely. In fact, the two are but two aspects of the same thing. When you have learned the techniques of relaxation, you will see that your mind floats free of tension as your body lies free of muscle tension.

The first thing to do is to relax the muscles of your head: the forehead, the face, the neck, the scalp and ears. Relax these areas one at a time.

You have to learn what the relaxation of a muscle feels like so that you can control it. To do this, start with your forehead. Tense these muscles as tight as you can. Now relax them. Feel what it feels like to consciously relax these muscles. After a few experiments, you should be able to completely relax these muscles without first tightening them. Now, do the same thing with other muscles, working your way down from your head to your toes. Some muscles will be easier to relax than others—these are the muscles of which you have long been most conscious: your biceps, forearm muscles, your fist, buttocks, etc.

If you feel that any part of the body is particularly tense, try this: gradually stiffen the muscles through various degrees of tension—step by step —from moderate to intense, until they are completely tense, hard, and stiff. Then work down the range in the opposite direction, relaxing them step by step, slowly unstiffening these muscles— until you have achieved complete relaxation. Because the head muscles are among those most taken for granted, it is especially important that you master the control of these. Of course, it is also extremely important that you master control of the muscles involved in sexual intercourse, such as the buttocks, abdomen, legs, and so forth.

Should the tensing-relaxing exercises make your body ache, you are probably overdoing the tensing and not doing enough relaxing. Let the relaxation be the largest part of these exercises. Lie back and enjoy the sense of relaxation you achieve for each muscle. Enjoy the relaxation of your head muscles for several minutes before working on mastering other muscles. The same thing goes for each step in the relaxation trip down your body.

When a part of your body is completely relaxed, another person will be able to treat this part as if it were attached, not to a live person but to a rag doll. Your head will be loose enough to be rolled gently. Your arm will fall like a dead weight if someone lifts it into the air and lets go of it. If another person can note some resistance in any of these tests, then you are not fully relaxed—more work is needed.

Use these tensing-relaxing exercises once or twice a day for perhaps a month; you should find that

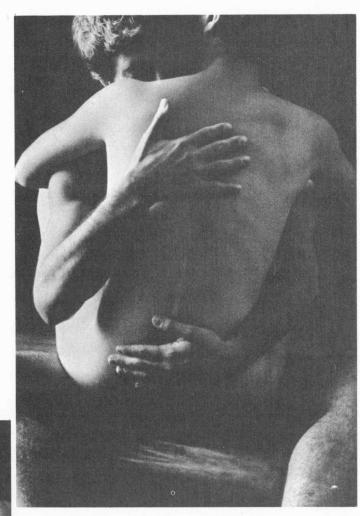

your body will be less susceptible to stiffness. And, when and if stiffness and tension do reappear, you will be able to deliberately relax your body in a very short period of time. Whatever technique you use to ease yourself, it must be done completely and totally. Sex cannot be successful if one or both of the partners is all tied up in knots. The result from that type of situation can only be disastrous. After all, ask yourself how you feel when you are very nervous and your intestines seem to be tied into the entire Boy Scout manual of knots—with a few Merchant Marine loops thrown in for free. Obviously you are ineffective and generally useless.

There are, then, three lessons you should learn from these exercises. First, you should become conscious of your body, so that you realize whether or not you are tense. Second, you should become able to relax yourself, physically and mentally— in other words, completely and totally—whenever you sense tension or stiffness developing. And, third—you should attain new mastery over the muscles that you use in your sex play. This should be a boon to you—and to your woman.

2 — It is most essential that you and your woman have your own private set of signals or communications. Each must know what the other is thinking and feeling; each must be aware that the other is near climax, and each must be utterly responsive to the other's needs and secret cravings. It is not enough to be aware of your partner's feelings. Obviously, they must be responded to, pampered, and used in your sex play. Your partner's cravings must be gratified, and they must also be made use of to gratify your own desires.

144

But you can't respond to something that you don't know about. So, first and foremost, the physical intimacy you share during sex play must be matched by an intimacy between your minds. You must learn to let each other know exactly what is being felt; you must also learn to understand the subtle signals your partner uses, both consciously and subconsciously. (In Babe Ruth's early days as a major league pitcher, he had an unconscious habit of licking his lips every time he was about to throw a curve. Sharp-eyed batters noticed this habit, and were always prepared for one of the Babe's curve pitches. Because they understood this little, unconscious gesture, they could get hits when they might otherwise have struck out. The same goes for you. Learn the signals that will allow you to belt one out of the park instead of striking out!)

Genital Twitching   Genital twitching is accomplished by contracting and relaxing your muscles at the bottom of the penis, about two inches in front of the rectum. These muscles can be contracted by trying to make your testicles and scrotum lift themselves right into your body. Before reading on, try this. Notice how easy it is to do. And notice the twitching effect this has on your penis, even if it isn't erect when you try it. When the penis is erect, the twitching will be even more pronounced.

It is possible to test whether the right muscles are contracting. Simply push one finger into the flesh to the rear joining of the scrotum to the body.

The greatest effect of genital twitching during intercourse comes from short, sharp, even jerky, twitches. This action should be learned carefully—which you may find easier to do after you have had some success with the relaxing-tensing muscle control exercises described above—and this twitching

145

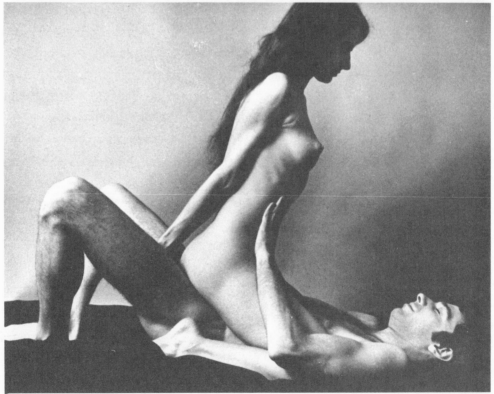

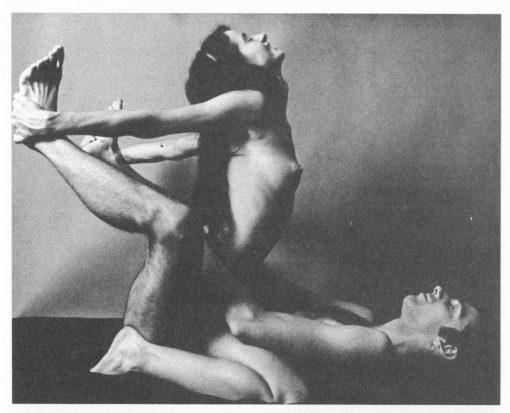

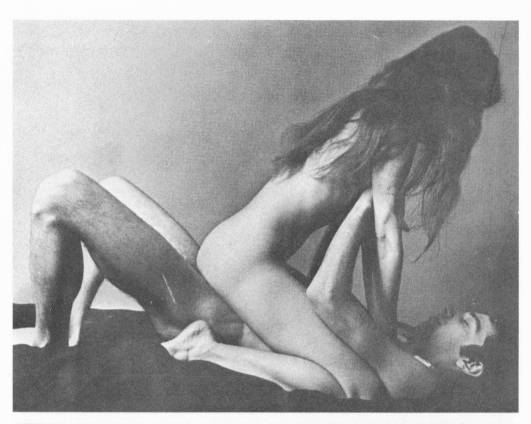

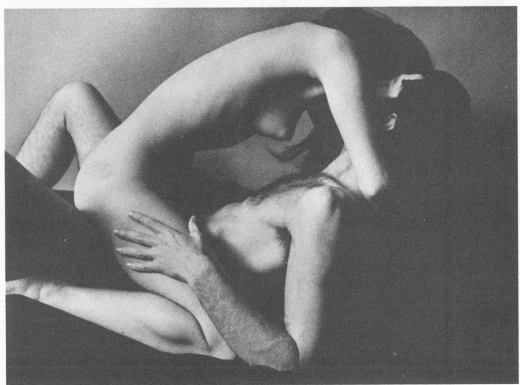

action should be practiced assiduously by snapping and exercising the muscles every day until you have complete mastery over this trick and this twitching becomes perfectly natural to you. Only in this way can muscle control be built up and your climactic control be developed.

Try this twitching-snapping during intercourse. At first, try it during pauses and rest intervals. It will act almost like an electric shock to help your woman maintain her passion and high level of excitement, without in any way hurrying your own climax. This technique can be used to have a long, drawn-out sexual intercourse which your woman will greatly enjoy and which will be within the control range of possibility for you. After penetration, keep your penis perfectly still within your woman. Do not use either in-and-out or sideways or circular motions. After a moment or two, begin the genital twitching, but do not use any other motion. Without either of you becoming fatigued and without chancing a premature ejaculation, you will create a delightful experience. Most couples will not want to use this method on a regular basis, but it provides an intriguing and pleasant change of pace. Usually, you will have some difficulty holding completely still, because the increasing passion of your woman as you twitch within her will drive her to motion—you'll have to hold on for dear life, just as if you were riding a rodeo bronco.

Another way of using this twitching trick is to try it at the depth of penetration during ordinary sexual intercourse strokes. Finally, after this technique has been mastered and fully developed, snap all the muscles that control your penis two or three times during a slow in-and-out stroke. Watch the effect this has on your woman.

In your woman's case, there are a variety of different genital motions that can be learned, and these can be combined in a number of different ways. It is very important that your woman work at developing her ability to control the muscles that allow genital motion. This can be the big difference between her being a mediocre sex partner and her being a

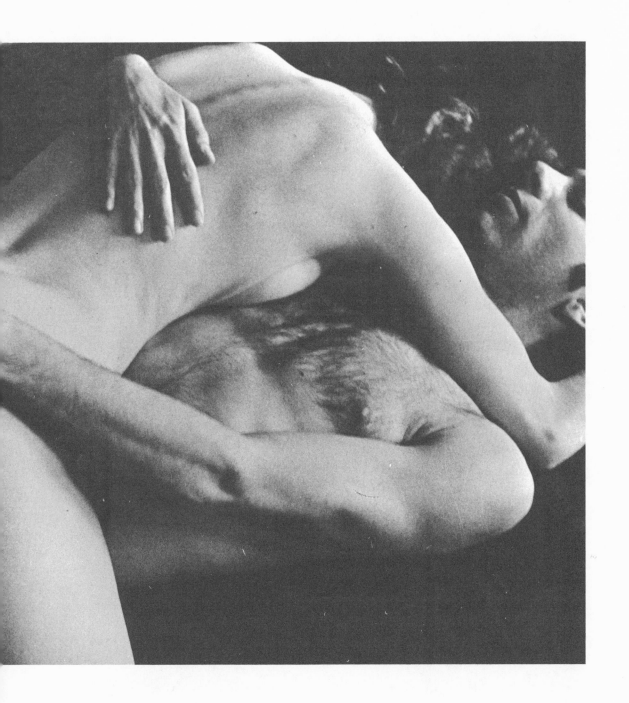

really great sex partner. Just as genital twitching on your part can enhance her pleasure during intercourse, her ability to control her muscles can add a great deal to the pleasure she gives you.

First of all, the easiest motion for her to try is done by trying to contract the rectum into her body. Done slowly, this contraction puts pleasant pressure on the penis within her vagina. But a rapid series of such contractions is what really has a delightful effect. As with a man, a woman can develop her ability in this area by practicing for a few minutes every day. This is quite easy to do, in that this exercise can be done at any time and almost anywhere, with no preparation at all.

It is quite a bit more difficult to control the muscles of the vagina and a great deal of concentration will be needed. But, remember, it is more than well worth the effort involved. These muscles can be contracted by trying to squeeze the vagina. This should be practiced every day until it is completely mastered. The contraction of the vaginal wall muscles during intercourse is not the point here. The important thing here is to build up these muscles and to develop muscle tone. This makes your woman a much more effective sex partner by creating what seems to be a tighter fit of the vagina walls around the penis and more stimulating action between the two organs during intercourse. Of course, this works to increase her pleasure during intercourse as well as increasing yours. But that, after all, is what dynamic intercourse and sexual power are all about. What is best for either of you will add to the pleasure of both of you.

If your woman works hard on mastering these contractions several times a day for a period of several weeks—and practices them seriously—she will become a far more effective and stimulating partner for you to enjoy. (Of course, it is up to you to make sure that you do your exercises during this period, so that both of you are the very best-in-bed that you can be.)

156

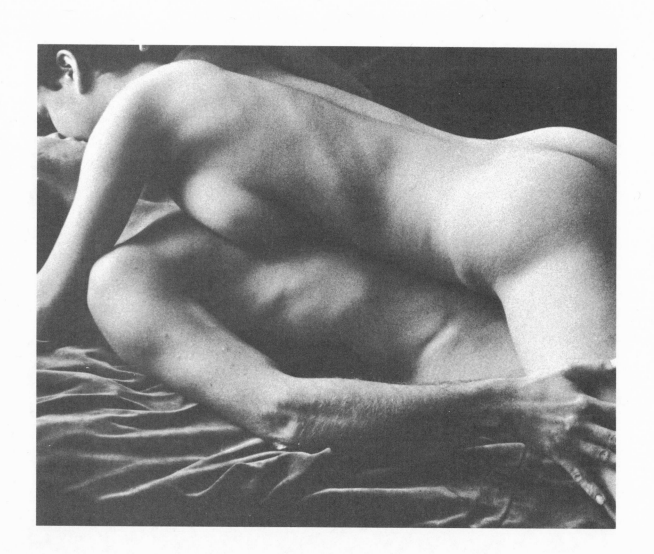

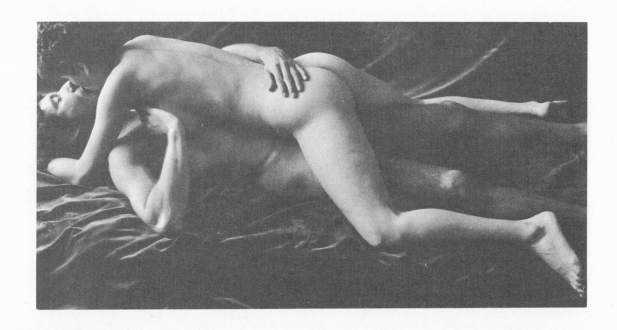

Breathing   The body uses up oxygen at a fast rate when the body is involved in vigorous activity, whether it be swimming, running, playing tennis, or having intercourse. This oxygen has to be replaced rapidly, and good breathing is important for a swimmer, runner, tennis player, or love-maker. A runner who is short of breath can't compete with runners in good condition. Likewise, a man or woman whos is short of breath can't be a great sex partner.

For this reason, it is extremely important that you develop good breathing techniques—if you want to be able to give your all on the fields of love. To accomplish this, brisk walks several times a week are of great value. Walk at a fast, steady pace, swinging your arms naturally, swinging your whole body into this exercise—and breathing deeply and regularly as you walk.

There are any number of other exercises that will help you develop good breathing techniques, but it is out of the scope of this book to go into all of them.

At least the following must be said, however: smoking and overweight are two excellent ways to shorten your breath and make you a less active and less satisfying sex partner. As far as heavy smoking goes, the warning on the sides of every pack of cigarettes might as well be changed to read: "Caution: Cigarette Smoking May Be Hazardous to Your Health—and to Your Sex Life."

Penetration   For many couples, sex play can be divided into two parts: foreplay, when both partners passionately stimulate each other and build up to a fever pitch; and intercourse, an essentially mechanical activity with only one purpose in mind —orgasm. Between the two stages, there is a brief, but awkward, change of positions and change of mood. This is a foolish waste of sexual energy!

Intercourse is the height of sex play. It shouldn't be mechanical, it shouldn't mark the end of mutual stimulation, and there

160

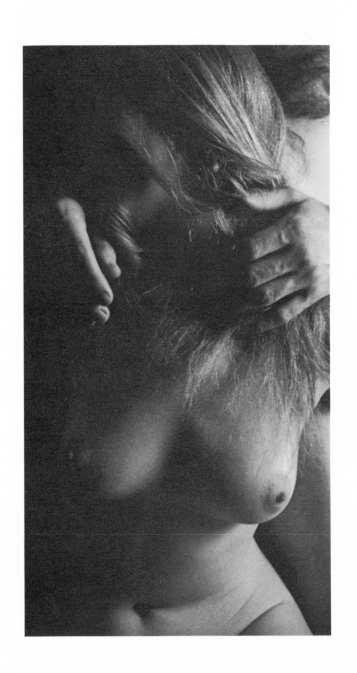

should be no cooling of mood. This is most important. The few moments of changing position and the act of penetration should not be a signal for a cooling off. And it is up to the man to see that the passions built up during foreplay are *heightened*—not weakened—during these few moments.

It is important that you continue your love-play even after foreplay has yielded to penetration. And the most effective way to do this is to take your time in making penetration, using your penis as a tool to excite the outside as well as the inside of your woman. You can gently massage the vaginal entrance, and even the clitoris, with your penis before plunging in. You can tease the vagina with the tip of your penis, penerating very slightly, then withdrawing to tease the outside, the lips or the clitoris. In this fashion, the act of penetration may take several minutes before it is completed—your woman's passion and desire for complete penetration increasing as you go on.

(Some women enjoy having the penis withdrawn during intercourse, to massage the clitoris for a moment, and then re-enter.)

There are times when a fast, deep peneration is desired by both the man and the woman. But, even in this case, it is still important that this act be a deliberate and passionate act—not a mechanical business to be gotten over without passion.

One other thing that you can do is to use genital twitching during a slow, steady penetration. Or you can use a rotating, screwing motion during a slow, steady penetration. In doing this, your penis explores the entire area through which it passes, pressing directly against the vaginal walls as well as forcing its way between them.

If there is not sufficient lubrication, you or your woman—or both of you—will feel the pain of friction and stretching. If this happens, you should withdraw and return to foreplay until your woman's increased passion results in better lubrication.

161

5

The
Dangers
of
Fear

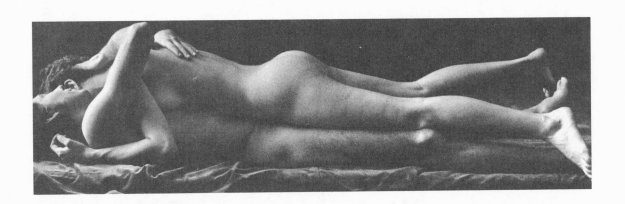

FEAR can ruin sex. It can spoil your self-confidence and take the edge off your woman's passion potential. It can distract either of you from full concentration on the act of love. It can cause tension that ruins your pleasure and lessens your ability to perform at peak sexual power. It can turn you into an ineffective lover and turn your woman into an unresponsive bed partner.

The conquest of fear—the elimination of fear—is a key part of attaining full sexual power and complete enjoyment from sexual relationships. It is your job, as the man, to conquer your own fears and help guide your woman into conquering hers.

Fear of Frigidity and Female Fear of Failure

Many couples worry about frigidity. When a woman doesn't have an orgasm by the end of the first week or so of marriage (or of living together), she might begin to worry about whether something is wrong with her sexual makeup. Anxiety sets in and grows rapidly, and this builds up within her even more rapidly as she encounters the sexual setbacks that become inevitable as anxiety replaces passion as the dominant emotion during sex play. Fear grows on fear, feeding on itself, and the result is enormous sexual unhappiness. This is a vicious circle that must be broken if any sexual happiness is ever to be achieved.

Very often, it is wise to scale down slightly these expectations of what can be achieved in the marriage bed. Of course, the new, more realistic expectations may be surpassed in the weeks and months to come, but it is foolish and destructive to demand more of yourselves than you are now likely to immediately achieve. Remember, love-play is play, not an Olympic game or contest. Don't set goals to reach or records to be broken; just relax and enjoy yourselves. Neither you nor your woman should *demand* that she have an orgasm. Just enjoy the sex play and let orgasms come—or not come—as they may. Remember: an opera may have a grand finale, but that isn't all there is to it. The music in the first and second acts isn't just a buildup to the finale—they're there to be enjoyed, too.

The woman who sees the orgasm as the test of her sexuality will probably be too tense to have one. The man who demands an orgasm from his woman—as a proof of her love or his skill—is putting so much pressure on his woman that she can't be expected to reach her climax. Some couples will go through all sorts of calisthenics and routines they heard about in order to bring the woman to climax. These couples are replacing mechanics for passion and it is unlikely that they will ever succeed.

There are, of course, cases of actual frigidity, and if you have real reason to suspect its presence you should send your wife to her gynecologist for help. But most "cases of frigidity" are nothing but *fear of frigidity* getting the upper hand in a woman's mind. It is fear of frigidity—rather than frigidity itself—which is the widespread problem. And it is up to you to help your woman conquer this irrational fear.

First, be sure that you don't do anything to encourage this fear. Don't keep asking your woman, "Did you, huh, did you?" Don't make her feel that she is failing you if she fails to reach climax. And don't let your fear that her "frigidity" is your fault drive you to make a big deal out of her lack of orgasms.

Also, be sure that the tenderness you show your woman before

166

intercourse is matched by tenderness afterwards. Make sure that you help her relax in her attitude toward sex. The elimini-nation of tension and anxiety is the way to help her overcome this problem.

Some women have a fear of "failure" in bed. That is, they are afraid that they don't satisfy their men. Of course, this fear also produces tension, and in fact makes these women less responsive, less satisfying partners. Once again, it is up to the man to show his woman that sex is not a contest and that he isn't judging her sexual abilities. The woman must simply be made to forget about her fears, relax, and enjoy herself. Once she starts enjoying sex instead of being self-conscious about her part in it, she will become a more re-sponsive, more passionate, and more effective partner.

Male Fear of Failure Many men fear that they will be impotent or that they will ejaculate prematurely or that they will be ineffecttive lovers. As in the case with women, the fear often causes the problem to occur. Fearing the inability to have an erection (or maintain it) at the right moment often prevents a man from having an erection. Fear of reaching climax prematurely often causes a man to ejaculate as soon as, or before, peneration is accom-plished. And fear of being a "lousy lover" often keeps a man so tense that he performs badly in bed.

There are many possible causes of impotence in man: it is beyond the scope of this book to deal with the deep-seated psychological problems that underlie various cases of im-potence. The point is, however, that many men experience what they think is impotence simply because they are afraid of this happening. The answer to this is relaxation: relax the fears and anxieties away. The relaxation exercises described in Chapter 4 may be of some help. And it may also help to just remember that many men have experienced temporary impotence, so don't be embarrassed, don't be scared, and don't think that your masculinity is any the less because you experience what so many other men experience.

167

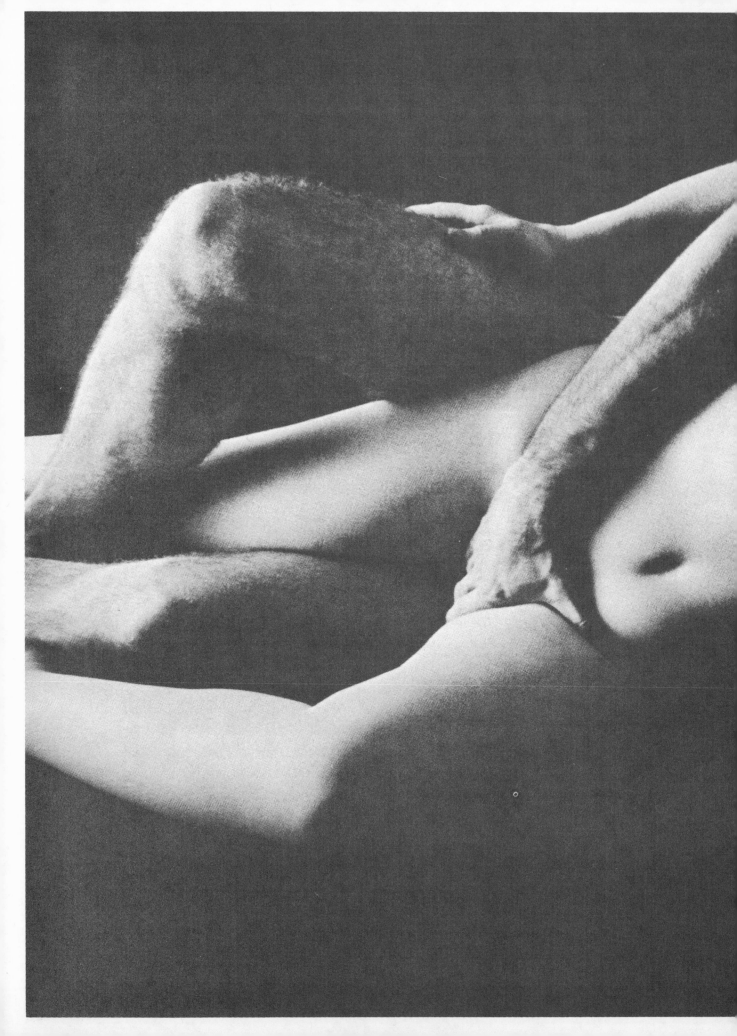

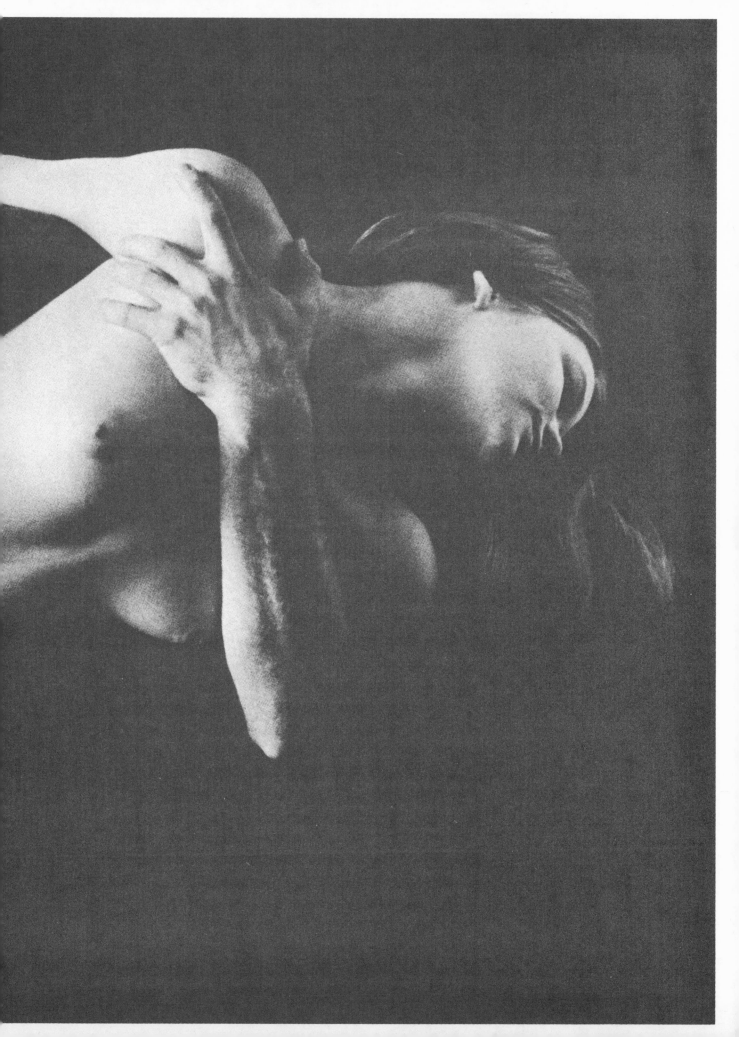

Chapter 4 also suggested some ways to lengthen the time before climax and these methods may help you overcome the problem of premature ejaculation. But it is also important that you don't get worried, anxious, and tense about reaching climax too soon. After all, the reason this book deals with this situation is that so many men—maybe all men—experience this at one time or another; a high percentage of men experience it relatively often. The one thing you shouldn't do is worry about it or be afraid that it will happen. The resulting tension is almost certain to make you lose control and ejaculate even sooner.

Of course, there are men who aren't impotent and who don't ejaculate too early very often—but who are still afraid that they are failures in bed. This fear is more foolish than the others. There are certain things you can do to make you a better lover—this book gives you many useful suggestions in that line—but the one thing not to do is worry or be afraid. After all, you can't throw yourself completely into love-play if your mind is filled with fears, worries, and anxieties. So concentrate on giving pleasure to your woman and taking pleasure for yourself and don't worry whether or not you are the "Champion." If you just enjoy yourself and give pleasure to your woman, that's enough. Just as for women, it is important for men not to set too high or unreasonable standards or expectations for their side of the marriage bed. Try relaxing and forgetting these irrational fears—you'll find that there wasn't ever anything to fear (except fear itself, as FDR said).

Fear of Injury to the Genitals Sometimes, great damage can be done by fear of injury to the sexual organs. For example, some women are afraid of fingernail stimulation of their genital area, believing that the slight scratching might damage them. This problem can be avoided by making sure that your fingernails are neatly trimmed, with no jagged edges to cause irritation. Again, many women are afraid of sexual injury through the stretching of delicate tissues by poorly oiled sexual frictions. Therefore, while the vaginal region is usually quite moist with natural liquids, especially after sufficient stimulation, the man should take care that any dryness is treated with adequate lubrication

172

so that there is no chance of painful friction. If the woman has the problem of building up the necessary degree of sexual passion, then it follows almost automatically that she will have a problem in generating enough natural fluid within her, so always remember to make sure that the woman is well supplied with a lubricant, either natural or artificial, to overcome the chance of possible pain and discomfort wihch she might otherwise feel—and which would dampen all passions.

Fear of Offending the other Partner

This is probably the most foolish sexual fear of all, and its solution is the simplest. Nevertheless, many couples have less than satisfactory sexual relations because one or both partners are afraid of shocking or offending the other partner. More often than not, the secret craving that is involved is the simplest thing possible. For instance, if a man fails to stimulate his woman's clitoris, she may think it is "perverted" of her to ask him to. She is afraid that the request will shock or offend her man. This is, of course, foolish. Both partners should feel free to communicate all desires, wishes, and tastes. After all, marriage isn't a partnership among strangers. If you are sharing physical intimacy, you should make the most of it by sharing a complete intimacy—one that allows the physical intimacy to be most satisfying.

Some men are afraid of offending their women by suggesting a position for intercourse that is not the "normal" position. This is just as foolish as the woman who won't ask her husband to stimulate her clitoris. After all, *both* of you share a mutual interest in having the most pleasurable sex. Why not share your ideas about how to accomplish this?

Some couples lose out on maximum sexual pleasure because one of the partners is afraid of offending the other by pointing out something unpleasant about her (or him). For instance, if there is something your woman does in bed that you don't like, it's better to tell her than to allow this to spoil your sex life. If one partner has bad breath or body odor that displeases the other partner, go ahead and say something about it. Isn't it silly to feel free to have sexual intercourse with someone but be afraid to talk honestly with hat person? If fears of offending each other plague your sex life, then it

173

is important to learn the habit of communicating freely. And it is up to you, as the man, to make this important change in your relationship.

Fear of Revealing Emotions

The fear of revealing emotions has no place in the sex life of any adult couple—but, unfortunately, it has harmed the marriages of many who should have known better.

"Playing it cool" is thought of as a good thing by many people. But there is a time and place for everything—and there is a time and place for avoiding almost anything. The bedroom is no place for "playing it cool." Some women, however, will hardly ever let themselves go, for fear of exposing their feelings—even to their husband. Often, this is because the woman feels insecure in the marriage, and it is up to the man to make her feel safer—and safe enough to let go of her feelings.

This problem is probably more common among men, however. Many men feel that it is their role to be strong, silent, and cool. They feel that emotions are feminine. Of course, nothing could be more ridiculous! You enjoy knowing that your woman enjoys sex with you; she'll get pleasure out of knowing that she is pleasing you. Let her know how much you enjoy making love to her—and not just before and after your sex play, but freely and openly while you are making love. Don't feel that you have to recite love poetry while having intercourse, but just let yourself go, the way you want your woman to let herself go.

The main problem about this fear of exposing one's emotions is that the energy given to keeping feelings secret is energy lost to sex. This is a loss of sexual power and has no place in your sex life.

Fear of Being Discovered

Adolescents engaged in premarital sex often dilute the pleasure of that sex with the fear of being discovered. But married couples—especially those who live with in-laws or who have children—still suffer from this fear. The desire for privacy is a natural thing, and it is unfortunate when circumstances force the fear of discovery into the married life of a couple.

175

The lack of privacy is a difficult problem and the resulting harm to the sexual relationship is serious. It is up to the couple to rearrange their schedule—or their furniture or their budget (by moving to less crowded quarters)—whichever is possible. The sexual relationship is an important part of marriage and a couple must do whatever is necessary to make it possible for them to share their love—without having to fear interruption by an outsider, even if the outsider is part of the family.

Of course, the fear of discovery can become a habit and continue even when it is no longer a realistic fear. In this case, it is obsessive and is in the province of a marriage counselor or psychologist—and beyond the scope of this book.

Fear of Pregnancy This is a very real fear for many women and it can ruin their sexual pleasure. A woman who has good reason to not want to get pregnant cannot be expected to throw herself with complete abandon into an act that may cause her pregnancy. Fortunately for most women, there is something very simple that can be done to eliminate this fear. That something is contraception. Of course, there are some women whose moral beliefs prohibit the use of contraception, and for these women there is a more difficult situation. They can rely on the "rhythm" method—if they find this to be moral—but the method is far from perfect and the fear of pregnancy may continue to haunt them and ruin their sexual pleasure. According to this method, the woman has intercourse only at the "safe" point in her period. Unfortunately, it is often difficult or impossible to be sure of the "safe" period, and pregnancy often occurs.

Aside from those women who are morally committed to not using contraception, there are women who cannot legally get contraception because of local laws. For these women there are only three possible legal solutions: don't have sex *or* get pregnant *or* move to a place where contraception is legal.

Of course, most women are not restricted by either a moral

ban or a legal ban. Many churches advocate the use of contraception and most localities either permit it or encourage it.

For women who are legally, morally, and medically in a position to use contraception, it is the best way to eliminate the fear of pregnancy and permit more relaxed, more pleasurable sex. There are several forms of contraception now available.

The condom, or male contraceptive is the least trustworthy. Unless there are compelling reasons to rely on this method, it should be avoided, in favor of a better method. In addition to its untrustworthiness, it decreases the pleasure of intercourse—especially for the male, whose penis is sheathed from direct contact with those wonderful walls of the vagina. Besides this, the chances of breaking this device are greatly increased if the penis is used to massage the outside of the woman's genitalia, so there are serious limits on what you can do when wearing such a device. The penis, for instance, should be withdrawn carefully immediately after the male orgasm, to prevent the device from slipping off a penis that has shrunken in size even slightly.

The diaphragm is also not completely safe, although it is more reliable than the condom. Too vigorous movement can displace this device, which must remain covering the entrance to the womb in order to do any good. In addition, there is a time element involved in the use of this device, in that more vaginal cream should be added after each intercourse. A night of complete abandon is not possible with complete safety. Finally, the vaginal cream needed when this device is used means that oral-genital relations cannot be had during the same session as intercourse, unless the woman gets up and inserts the device after having oral-genital relations and before intercourse. This most certainly can ruin the sex play.

An intrauterine coil is available, but there is some dispute about the safety of this. Your doctor will be able to give you a fair view of the values and possible dangers of the coil.

177

For most couples, the contraceptive pill is best. This is an almost completely certain way of preventing pregnancy, if prescribed and taken as directed. There are several brands and strengths and your doctor will guide you to the best one for your woman. There are some side effects, but most women can take the pill with relative safety. The great advantage of the pill is that it provides a way of eliminating the fear of pregnancy without interfering in the sex play at all.

Many couples whose sex lives have been damaged by the fear of pregnancy have found a whole new world of intimacy and gratification since the advent of the pill.

If there are not moral, legal, or medical reasons to avoid the pill, this is an essential step in creating a sexual relationship that is not harmed and diluted by fear of pregnancy.

The reader is warned, however, to rely on your doctor's advice. There are sometimes medical reasons for avoiding the pill. For instance, new mothers who want to nurse their infants should avoid the pill, which sometimes has the effect of cutting off the milk supply or the nutritional content of the milk. And there are women whose chemical makeup or physical condition make it unwise to take the pill. So be sure to rely on your doctor's advice in this matter.

One short warning should be given about a form of "birth control" that doesn't work at all. This is the technique of withdrawal, in which the man withdraws his penis immediately before ejaculating. Unfortunately for those who rely on this little trick, there already is some leakage of semen into the woman's body long before the approach of orgasm. All that this technique accomplishes for certain is to decrease both partners' pleasure. And there is a not-so-funny joke that sums up the effect of this technique: Question— "What do you call a couple that uses the withdrawal method of birth control?" Answer—"Parents!"

6

Male
Capacity

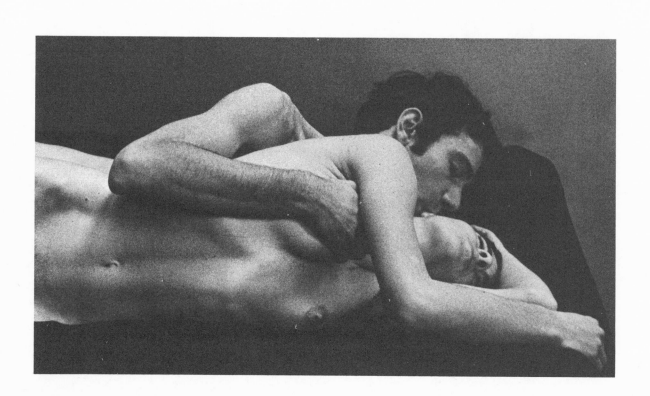

EVERY man wants to possess virility like that possessed by few of his fellows. Every man, including you, craves the power to enter a woman again and again and again, satisfying her completely each time. Every man wishes he were virile enough to feel that he is just getting started after his third climax—instead of being finished after his first or second. Every man wishes he were up to the feats described in the local bar, in the college dormitory, or in the factory lunchroom—even though most men realize that many of these feats of sexual extravagance are more exaggeration than fact.

To a great extent, this capacity to enter a woman again and again and again is determined by the man's ability to control himself and to regulate his own orgasm. Within reasonable limits, any man can increase his sexual capacity by making a conscious effort to increase his self-control and his control over his orgasms.

In this respect, you are faced with three particular problems. First, you are very rapidly aroused. Second, you are even more quickly satisfied. Third, your desire for further sex play almost always drops drastically after your ejaculation. Your woman, of course, is entirely different—and, as Hamlet said, there lies the rub. It takes a woman a longer time to become aroused to a high excitement level. It generally takes a woman longer to have her sexual excitement build to the point of climax. And most women are capable of experiencing more

183

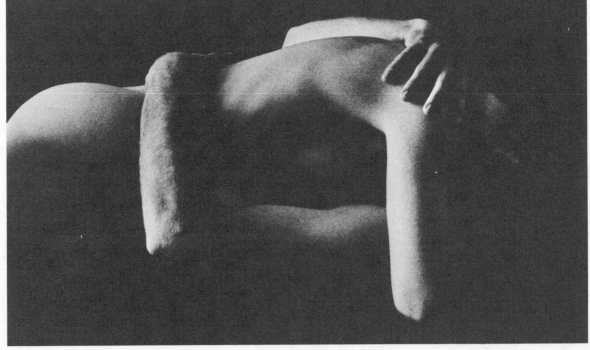

orgasms over a relatively short time period than most men. Women may experience a drop-off in sexual excitement and desire after reaching a climax, but this drop-off is usually gradual rather than sharp. In short, women take longer to get there, but once they get there they don't leave so soon.

Thus, the problem faced by just about every man is to pace himself properly and to hold himself in complete control when he needs to. Fortunately, there are ways of dealing with each of the three areas of imbalance between a woman's sexual timing and your own. First, you should give the woman a headstart through a long, slow session of foreplay, in which you concentrate on raising her level of excitement. Of course, if you allow her to stimulate your genitals as much as you stimulate her during this time, you will defeat the entire purpose of what you are doing. Use the foreplay to give your woman an excitement edge over you. She takes longer to get there, so you have to let her start first on the road to high sexual excitement. Of course, stimulating a woman can be very exciting, but you should take advantage of the slow pace to control yourself. You must deliberately hold down your own excitement during this period.

Now, suppose we deal with the problem of premature ejaculation—normally a problem with youths who have had very little sexual experience, and to whom the mere touch of a woman's body provides enormous sexual excitement, and also those men who are high-strung and whose nerves are far more sensitive than is good for them. (As you can see, the situation here is still the same as in trying to give your woman a headstart—deliberately holding down your sexual excitement is the key to solving this.) Not just youths and highly nervous men experience this problem. Every normal man will on occasion experience premature ejaculations. This will occur perhaps when a man has been without sexual intercourse for a prolonged period of time and all these feelings are built up within him to the point where the mere touch of a woman's body will send him over the brink. Or, he will pace himself improperly and so will ejaculate before the proper time.

Sometimes, too, a man who might be used to a rather passive woman will come into contact with a highly passionate partner who might cause him to ejaculate almost immediately. (In fact, this would be the case with almost any man who has limited his sexual activity to only his wife and who has come to feel rather stale with this one partner.) This added touch of variety in another woman would very easily cause him to become highly excited. After all, if a change of women doesn't add extra excitement, why bother switching? So remember, watch yourself with a new woman! Also, even the same woman you are used to may act particularly responsive one time and have the same effect.

If you feel you are about to "go off" too soon, force yourself to think about something unrelated to sex. For example, think about last night's dinner. Or Vietnam! Or your income taxes!! *That* is sure to cool off your excitement. Some men use the multiplication tables, thinking to themselves: two times two is four, two times three is six, two times four is eight, and so forth. This has the advantage of helping you keep up the rhythms of sex without keeping up all the excitement. It is best if you have something that you rely on to think about at times like this, so that you are all ready to use this cooling-off device before the thermometer explodes.

At any rate, no man should worry about the occasional premature orgasm. (Just be sure to keep in mind that overexcitement in love play cause ejaculation before insertion. You are not the only man about whom this is true. Almost all men, except those with special psychological problems that prevent them from fully participating in the excitement of sex play, are easily triggered. So, ejaculating before insertion, as a result of overly exciting love play, can not in any way be called premature. As a man, you can take only so much excitement before you go off. "Premature," in the sense in which we are discussing the word, refers to occasions when men will reach orgasm sooner than can be normally expected, when the man can do something to control himself—if he knows how to do this.)

187

In considering the man and woman as a sexual unit, self-control is absolutely necessary on the part of the man. You are, as a man, in the position to consider the sexual satisfaction that you will provide your partner, and this involves careful control of the speed with which you reach an orgasm. This consideration for your partner is absolutely necessary if you are to be successful in bed. This is essential, in fact, if you have the normal male ego that desires a reputation of being known as a man for whom women crave—at least, a man whom your own woman craves. Obviously, if you merely regard a woman as a means to satisfy your own passion—as quickly and one-sidedly as possible—and nothing more, then your partner will be faced with a rather unexciting sexual experience. Even if you are so selfish that you only care about your own pleasure, you should realize that you can't get as much pleasure from a turned-off woman as you can from a turned-on wildcat of a woman in bed. For one thing, it is very exciting and pleasant to feel your woman reach her climax, and it is best—for you as well as for her—if her climax comes before, or at the same moment as, yours.

Of course, some men have the idea that the size of their penis is enough to make them extremely desirable and satisfying. Do you like to think of your penis as a clenched fist? Then give up deluding yourself about its size—and about the value of its size. Aside from an obvious curiosity value that will certainly attract women to begin with, no large penis by itself is going to make a woman happy. (Just as a man with a smaller penis need not fear that he cannot please a woman as well as his oversized friend can.) The size of the penis is not the important thing. What is important is knowing how to use it. It is your skill with the tool, rather than the size of the tool, that determines how well you do the job. Don't fool yourself into thinking that a woman will be satisfied with a few clumsy strokes delivered with a large penis; whatever the size, she will want more than a few strokes and not clumsy ones, at that.

190

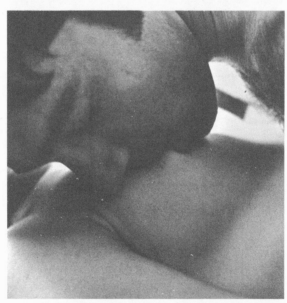

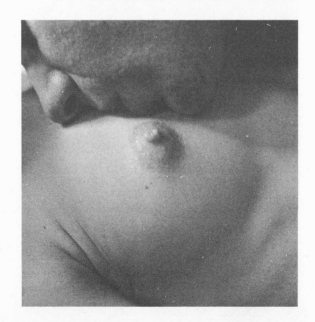

You may well find the sight of your partner very pleasing and exciting, especially with the right amount of clothing off and in the right setting. Nevertheless, the sight of her is never enough to trigger your sexual release. Contact with that delightful body, however, is quite another matter. Therefore, you must be very careful of the amount and type of motion that you engage in when you first clasp your partner to you and you both roll and glide your bodies against each other, clasping and clenching and caressing. Remember not to "attack" your partner too vigorously at the beginning! And, just as important, if your partner is particularly aggressive in bed, don't let her get to you too soon, and don't let her do the exciting things that will rush you to orgasm. Assert yourself and set the pace that you know you need for the purpose of controlling your own excitement while increasing hers. Be gentle and relaxed. (Here's one place where your relaxation exercises will come in very handy.) Search and explore and fondle—but keep the more vigorous motions for later. Be very careful about how your partner fondles your genitals at the beginning. Of course it is delightful, but always save the treats until dessert time. If you have been experiencing orgasms too soon for a while, you're probably better off completely denying yourself the pleasures of having your genitals touched during foreplay. If your woman feels deprived because you won't let her fondle you, just remind her that she'll be glad later on when you have more to give her when she really craves it. Also, if your woman likes to handle your scrotum or tease your buttocks while you are having intercourse—and these actions usually rush men toward the climax —you should ask her to refrain from these teasing actions. At least until you have mastered better control over yourself and your orgasms, deny yourself the extra stimulation that causes you to climax too soon.

As soon as you feel involuntary spasms in your penis, and certainly no later than when you first feel that delightful, soft, tingling sensation at the head of the penis, be sure to immediately stop all bodily motions and switch your concentration

away from the excitement of your love-play. To play very safe, you should stop the climb to orgasm every time you feel that you are anywhere near the peak.

To illustrate this problam—and it *is* a problem—let us use the simile of the automobile. It takes great power to get the car moving, increasing its speed to a high velocity. But once it is moving at a high speed, the motor needs to apply only relatively small amounts of power in high gear to keep up the momentum of the automobile. In many respects, it is the same with a man's sexual power. Once his penis is hard and erect, and he is approaching the moment when he would ejaculate, it takes very little motion to keep him at this level, certainly much less than was necessary to bring him up to this level of hardness and excitation—even if it didn't take all that much to get him here, he can stay here with even less active stimulation. Therefore, once you are approaching the brink of the cliff, so to speak, you can drive right over without stepping on the gas at all. To stop before you reach the cliff's edge, you have to step on the brakes. You'll have to cut your rhythm down, perhaps even stopping completely, to ward off an unwanted ejaculation. Of course, your natural instincts at this point will be driving you to increase your speed and rush to completion. You'll have to overcome these instincts and hold yourself back. When an orgasm approaches, every instinct within you cries out for you to hurry it along, to seize your brief moment of ecstasy. But the test of whether or not you are a superior lover will be determined by whether or not you are able to suppress such instincts until the right moment. The sooner you shut off an oncoming climax, the easier it will be to overcome these instincts. Therefore, don't think you have to wait until the last second before you cut back. The last second will almost always be too late.

All of this should help you solve the problem of too-soon orgasms. But, unless you are careful and know what you are doing, you can create another problem. Cutting back on your rhythm—or stopping completely—can have the same cooling effect on your woman as you want it to have on you. Your partner's orgasm is totally dependent upon a steady, uninterrupted series of movements, and every interruption will reduce the pinnacles of her ecstasy. Especially, those interruptions which are designed to let one partner cool off are likely to cool the other partner, too.

One important thing you can do to help solve this problem is to keep your hands busy all the time during intercourse. In this way, your hands can take over some of the rhythms you stop delivering with your body and penis.

Ideally, you should aim for a situation where you are not completely poised on the edge of the brink (so that one extra motion would send you over). Thus you will not have to halt your rhythmic stimulation of your woman completely. By remaining back from the edge, you'll be able to participate in a steady, not-very-vigorous variety of motions, while at the same time doing your best to stimulate your partner with your fingers and mouth—or whichever of these is available for use in the position you have chosen.

Sometimes, a woman will want to be treated like a bucking bronco that you have to ride hard and fast. But, usually, a woman will get more satisfaction out of a slow, steady rhythm, especially if this pace helps you last long enough to do her a great deal of good. After you have mastered good control with your woman, you may find that you'll be able to hold out for a long time at a hard and fast pace—but don't worry about that until you are in complete control of yourself at the slower, steadier pace. You can see that Nature acts fairly in all this. Even though natural instincts drive you to a faster pace just when you should slow down, Nature also helps you out by having women prefer the slower pace that you need for self-control.

There is another important advantage to the slower pace. Your ability to control yourself is greater if you are not too tired. By going more slowly, you preserve the energy that you can direct toward the task of controlling yourself. From

this, you should also be able to see that your self-control will be better if you have intercourse at times when you are rested —and relaxed. Relaxation is important here because you can't devote as much energy to the task of controlling yourself if you are wasting energy on muscle tension.

If you have a very passionate wife who demands a great deal of sexual activity, and you have the problem of a relatively low level of potency, then there will obviously be serious friction within your marriage unless you take steps to plan your bedtime sessions so that your wife gets all she wants without your having to give more than you really have.

There are several ways to deal with this difficult situation, other than just letting the marriage decay and break apart. First, a man with a relatively low level of potency should consult his physician to find out whether this is caused by some physical problem which is draining precious energy and vitality away from the man's sexuality.

Beyond this, however, a man can change his sexual activity patterns so as to bring a better balance between his low level of potency and his wife's high level of sexual demands. Certainly, the man should devote more efforts to satisfying his wife with a love-play that doesn't rely heavily on the act of intercourse. He should use his hands, mouth, and imagination more, so as to take the burden off his area of sexual weakness. He should concentrate on giving pleasure in all the ways that don't bring him to climax but do satisfy his wife. Just coming to the conscious decisions to put the woman's satisfaction first, and the release of his own sexual tensions after that, will be an important first step. If your wife for some reason believes that you should avoid some of this fore-play and get to the "real thing," it will be up to you to show her just how real the pleasure she gets from foreplay can be. And you'll never be able to do this by sitting down and telling her or trying to argue with her. You'll just have to prove to her how much excitement you can provide with your mouth and hands.

196

Of course, all of this relates to the idea of living with your low potency level, rather than actually attempting to increase your potency. But, this is also important, and it is possible to do this.

If low sexual potency happens to be your particular problem, if you find yourself lagging in your attempts to keep up with your wife's desires, it should be obvious that all this stems from a lack of semen. Your body is not creating a great enough supply in a relatively short period of time. After all, you certainly are not able to create much sexual excitement unless you have a supply of semen ready for release. This is something you certainly must note immediately after reaching climax and ejaculating, when your penis changes from the powerful instrument of male sexuality to a part that is simply not very valuable as a way to stimulate your woman. With the depletion of your semen supply comes a noticeable depletion of your sexuality and sexual power. Of course, if your body can quickly replace this supply of semen, your sexuality and sexual power are quickly restored. If your semen supply cannot be replenished, then this quick restoration of sexual power is impossible.

Therefore, if you have the problem of low sexual potency, you have to somehow deal with the problem of short semen supply. The way to do this should be obvious. What you can't produce quickly, you must learn to spend less freely. In other words, you must guard your semen supply and make good, thrifty use of it. You must use only the smallest amount that you can. Think of the long distance runner: If he tries to sprint at the beginning of the race, he will never finish the course. He will collapse and fall by the wayside. Instead, a man who wants to run a long distance race—and still be in it at the finish—must start slowly, or at least steadily, so that his energy is not used up entirely at the very beginning.

Or take the example of budgeting money. If you earn $100 a week, you can spend the whole amount on payday. But, if you do this, you won't have any money to spend during the

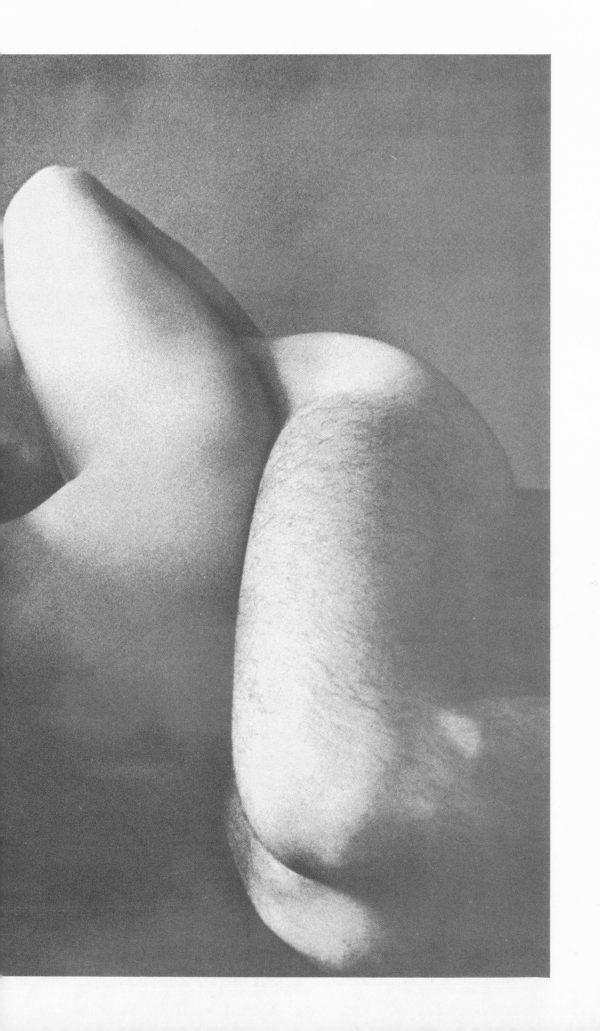

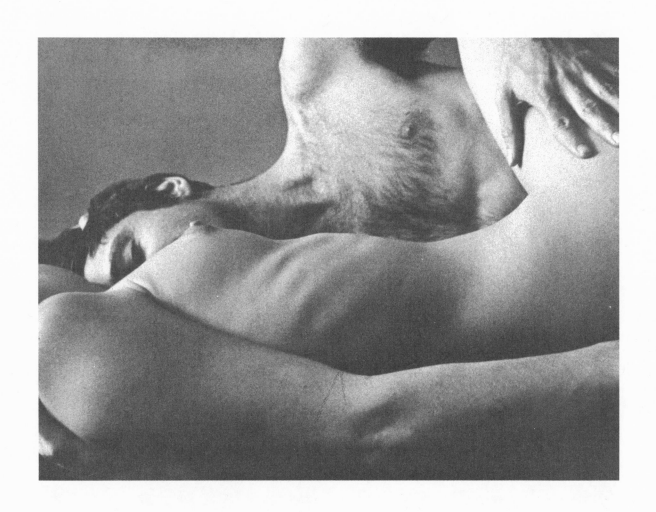

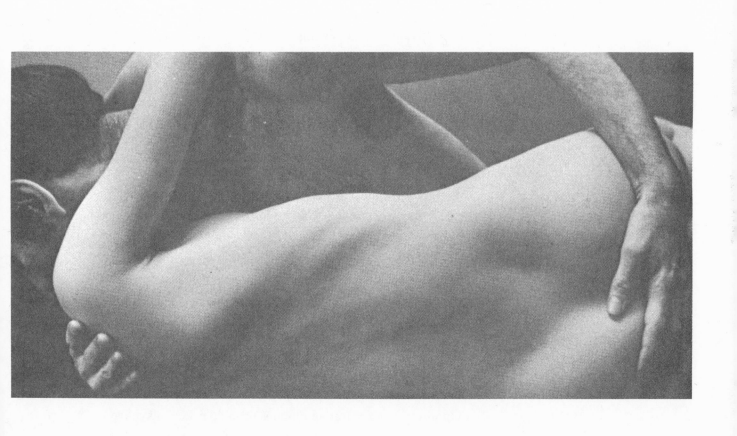

next six days. It will take you a whole week to replenish your money supply and, until you replenish it, you just won't be able to do any spending.

Well, that's the same thing as the problem of a limited semen supply. If you spend all your semen at once, you won't have anything to spend until your next "payday." But you can budget your semen, just as you can budget your money. By using less semen at first, you can make it possible to do some more spending—even before your body produces more.

Again, like the long distance runner, you don't give your all until you are ready to reach the very end of your race. The final burst of speed comes toward the end. So it is with a man who has a potency problem or, and this is very important, if you do not have such a difficulty but merely want to extend your activities over many hours. To accomplish this, therefore, you must cut down the outflow of semen during each orgasm. If you do this, and thus always have a supply of unused semen within you, you will thus be able to quickly once more raise up your semen level to the point where you are as sexually excited and ready to go again.

After all, low potency level is not, itself, the real problem. The real problem is the effect it can have on your ability to satisfy your woman. So, what you have to do is increase your ability to keep going in sexual activity, however high or low your potency level may be. There are men who have high levels of potency who do not take advantage of this to give their women the pleasures of long, drawn-out sessions. But this is what women enjoy: not the potency level of their men, but what their men do with those potency levels.

Women are naturally constructed so as to get their greatest pleasure from sex sessions that go on for a long time, rather than just a few, frustrating minutes. The "quickie" may give a man a way to achieve fast sexual release, but it is of little value to most women. So, the best thing to do is to cut back on your semen loss during each orgasm, so that you can provide your wife with the quantity of sexual activity to which she is deserving.

204

Remember, seminal retention has no bearing whatsoever on fertility. Neither you nor your wife will undergo any great lessening of orgasm with this procedure. The only disadvantage is that you will have a somewhat decreased and shorter period of sexual ease and contentment. You will find that you do not feel completely at rest and satisfied when you still have semen left within you. As a result of this, you will soon feel a need and desire for a renewed sexual joining—another drive toward sexual release. But, of course, this is the whole idea of seminal retention.

Now, let us look at how to practice the technique of seminal retention. If you are relatively inexperienced in sexual intercourse, you should not attempt this—at least until you have gained some more experience and mastery in sexual relations. You will find that it takes all your energies and concentration merely to go through the sex act as expertly and competently as possible without having to concern yourself with this particular technique.

To accomplish seminal retention, you will first have to master the control and use of your muscles. (For this reason, the exercises suggested in an earlier chapter will once again prove themselves well worth the energy involved in practicing them.) The key muscles in this case are the ones surrounding the urinary tube, which serve to hold the urine within your bladder until you are ready to release it. Now, these muscles are not like those involved in basic vital functions such as respiration and blood circulation—muscles which are controlled by the body without any conscious involvement. Nobody has to learn how to control the muscles of the heart that pump blood through the circulatory system. But the muscles controlling the retention of urine are voluntarily controlled—and control of them is learned (by most people) during the first few years of life. Once having learned this control in infancy, however, the human being learns to take this control for granted. So, you will have to once again gain a conscious awareness of the control you have over these muscles.

205

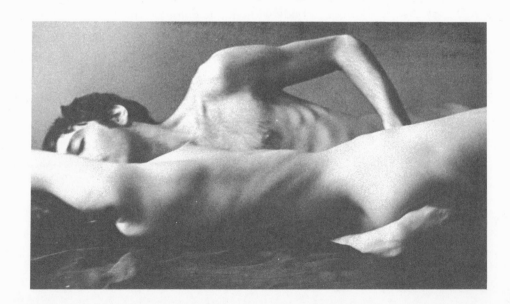

The method of gaining complete, conscious mastery over these muscles is to practice cutting off the flow of urine in the midst of emptying your bladder. Do this several times whenever you are urinating. Don't squeeze off the flow slowly and steadily. Let the flow come out hard and strong, then tighten your muscles and, so to speak, shut off the tap. Then release the flow completely, so that it is again hard and strong. Then shut it off again. Repeat this four or five times, if you can. Just make sure that when the urine flows, it flows completely freely and when it is shut off, it is shut completely.

There are other muscles involved and you will have to gain control and mastery over them. These are the muscles which help raise the scrotum up into the crotch and surround the base of the penis. Try lifting your testicles and the back part of your scrotum straight up into your body. As you do this, you will feel these muscles tightening up. Do this several times right now. Make yourself aware of what it feels like to tense and relax these muscles. You must learn to recognize this sensation in order to make possible conscious control. Try tightening these muscles very slowly and relaxing them very slowly. You should work to get complete control over these muscles, and this includes the ability to tighten or relax them quickly and sharply or slowly and steadily. These are muscles that you are probably not used to controlling consciously, so you will have to put some effort into strengthening your power of deliberate control over them. In so doing, you will also be strengthening the muscles themselves, which will be very helpful.

If you are to gain full muscle control, you must practice these two sets of exercises several times a day for several weeks, until you feel perfectly comfortable and natural in imposing your conscious will on these muscles. Even when you reach this point, you may still find some difficulty in shutting off your semen flow during ejaculation the first time you try to do this. Don't be surprised if you fail the first time (or even the first two or three times) you attempt to practice seminal retention. Return to your muscle control exercises and keep trying. Remember: you are trying to work against the natural instinct to allow complete sexual release. It may be difficult at first to overcome this instinct, but it can be accomplished if you keep working at it. And, once you gain this power, you will be able to use it almost every time you want to.

In addition to the muscle control involved, you will have to develop your sense of timing, so that you tighten the muscles and shut the tap just as soon as the ejaculation starts. Once you gain mastery over the muscles involved in this technique, however, the control of timing should be easy to learn.

Then, when you have reached the point where you have this complete physical control, you will be able to shut off your flow of semen in the midst of your final surge merely by tightening these muscles at the right moment. Your discharge of semen will be quite drastically cut without in any way interfering with various other sexual movements. Everything else should be done normally. Finish off the encounter as you normally would, but just make sure that you have a very tight grip on those muscles until your orgasm has been completed. If you do this, you will then not be emptying your reservoir of semen and you can refill it much faster. Your penis will lose much of its erection, but it is best that you continue mild caresses for a while, so that rapid loss of erection does not take place—which could allow some additional leakage of the fluid.

Do not worry that seminal retention will decrease the pleasure your orgasm gives to your partner. It is, of course, true that the male orgasm is a particularly delightful sensation for the woman within whose body this explosion takes place. But, seminal retention does not decrease the effect. The throbbing of the penis, which is especially exciting to the woman, still takes place. And the pleasant sensation of semen spurting against the vaginal walls still takes place. Even though the amount of semen involved is less, the pleasure it gives your woman will be just as great. And, more important, you will be able to return to intercourse after only a short wait.

209

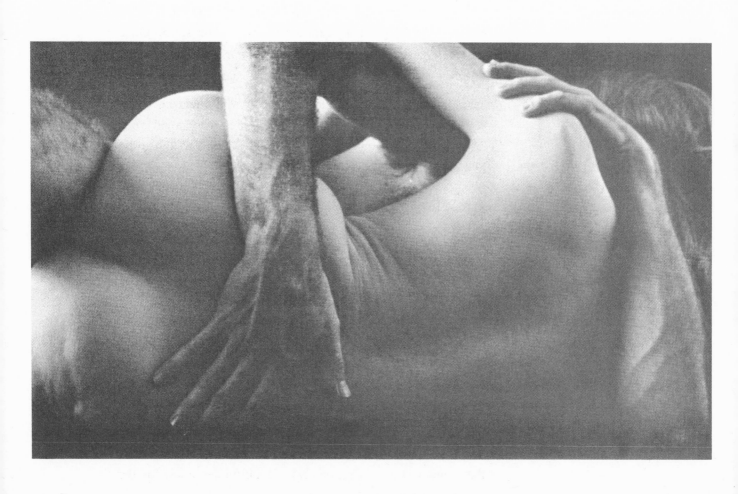

Even with a renewed semen supply, most men find that their orgasms do not come so quickly after the first one during each session. This is fortunate, because it means that the second time around will last longer—which your woman should appreciate. Of course, if there is not a long wait after your first climax, you may return to intercourse without much—if any—new foreplay. This has the advantage of making use of your woman's still high level of excitement without raising yours to the brink of a new orgasm.

7

Intercourse: Positions and Movement

The woman on her back positions

FOREPLAY is a time for imagination and experimentation, a time to try everything, to linger over any technique that gives pleasure, a time to throw yourself fully into the giving and receiving of ecstasy. Unfortunately, many couples end this experimenting and carefree pleasure-seeking when they move from foreplay to intercourse. This is ridiculous! Variety, experimentation, and changes of pace and style have just as much place in the act of intercourse as in the various acts leading up to it.

Remember: after a smorgasbord of appetizers, you don't want to serve cheese sandwiches as a main course.

Choosing the Sexual Position

There is a time and place for everything, including the various sexual positions. If either you or your woman is sexually inexperienced, it is recommended that the use of assorted postures should follow a certain sequence that allows you to get sexually comfortable with each other before trying more complex or more acrobatic sexual experiments. The first times together, you should use some sort of face-to-face side position, while you make sure that your climax is controlled. The next step, once your climax is perfectly under control—or almost perfectly, at any rate—is to achieve a mutual sexual climax. At this stage, the best position is for your wife to be on her back, although the preliminaries can be conducted from another position—or, more likely, from a series of other positions, as the two of you allow your sensations to drive your bodies against each other in constant motion, rolling, gliding, and pressing against each other.

215

At about the same time as you start trying the woman-on-her-back positions, you should also try some woman-on-top position, as the vagina will be partially stretched by this time, allowing entry with your woman above you. Again, it doesn't matter what positions you have been using in fore-play, in that you can roll your woman onto her back or roll your woman onto her back or roll her up on top of you before penetration is made.

The next step is to master the more complicated, synchronized movements, especially those that are used in the woman-on-the-back positions. You will probably find that most woman can master this stage without any serious difficulties—although you shouldn't be worried or surprised if inexperience shows itself in some clumsy ways. Relatively inexperienced lovers often find their sexual sessions interrupted by accidental withdrawal, improper insertion, and any number of other awkward little accidents that shouldn't really cause either worry or embarrassment.

After you have both mastered the basic positions and the movements that go with these, you should experiment with all sorts of sexual positions with all the variations you can think of or accidentally discover.

Naturally, this will all add variety to your sexual life, which is absolutely essential to any prolonged sexual relationship. If you are young and relatively inexperienced, and still exploring and being uncontrollably excited by intercourse in the basic few positions, you will find it hard to believe that sex actually becomes dull, boring stuff to some couples. But it is true. Achieving intercourse in the very same way, with the same partner, time after time after time, kills most passion and excitement. And there is nothing duller than dull sex.

From your own point of view, at least one of two factors are needed to keep the passion and ecstasy in sex: variety in intercourse with the same woman and/or variety in women. And any woman who does not recognize this is incredibly

216

stupid because she is throwing away the future success of her marriage. Hardly any men will endure boredom in their marriage beds without very quickly doing something about it. If a wife can't or won't fulfill the sexual needs of her husband, it is usually pretty certain that the husband will find some other woman who can and will give him what he needs and wants. Naturally, faithfulness to one woman is a very debatable proposition in itself. If you, as a man, wish to be faithful to your woman, then this is very commendable. But man, being the animal that he most certainly is, will for the most part crave variety—and he'll find it. If he has been stale with his wife, a little stimulating variety with another woman will do wonders for the marriage—for the woman as well as the man. Thus, any woman who is prepared to go into shrieking hysterics or, just as bad, into a grouching sulk, when she learns that her man has been sharing other beds is very stupid, indeed. Not only will such a wife drive her husband further away—because the contrast between the hysterical or sulking atmosphere in her home and the loving and sexual atmosphere with the other woman will appear very striking—but because she will not learn the lesson she should learn if she wants to keep her man. That lesson is that she has to provide sexual variety at home if she doesn't want her husband to seek it elsewhere. The wife should realize that if her man's emotional state benefits from sexual variety—at home and elsewhere— her own emotional state will benefit, too.

Sexual Movements

There is obviously a very limited variation of sexual movements that can be carried on within the confines of our physical structures. Nonetheless, you should try to get full value out of these variations that are possible, no matter how limited the variation is. What can be varied are: direction of movement, speed, rhythm, and extent of movement.

In terms of direction, the basic movement is forward and backward, with the penis moving deeper into the woman and withdrawing from the full depth. However, this is not the only movement direction. The man may also use a circular,

217

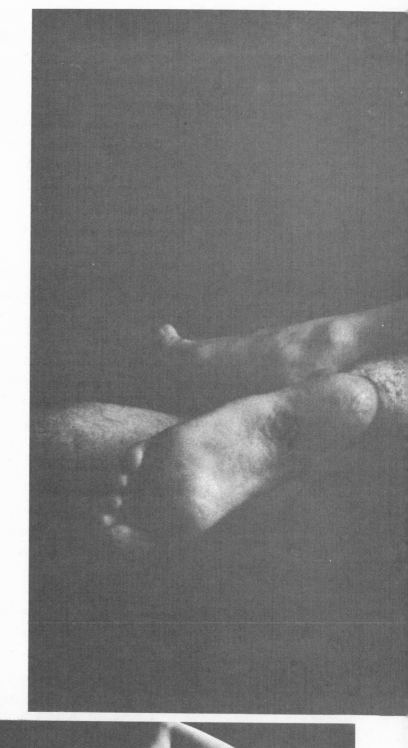

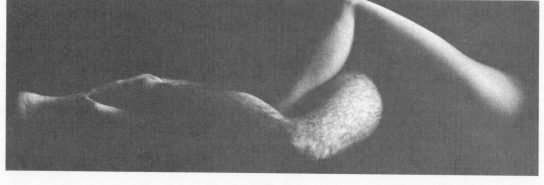

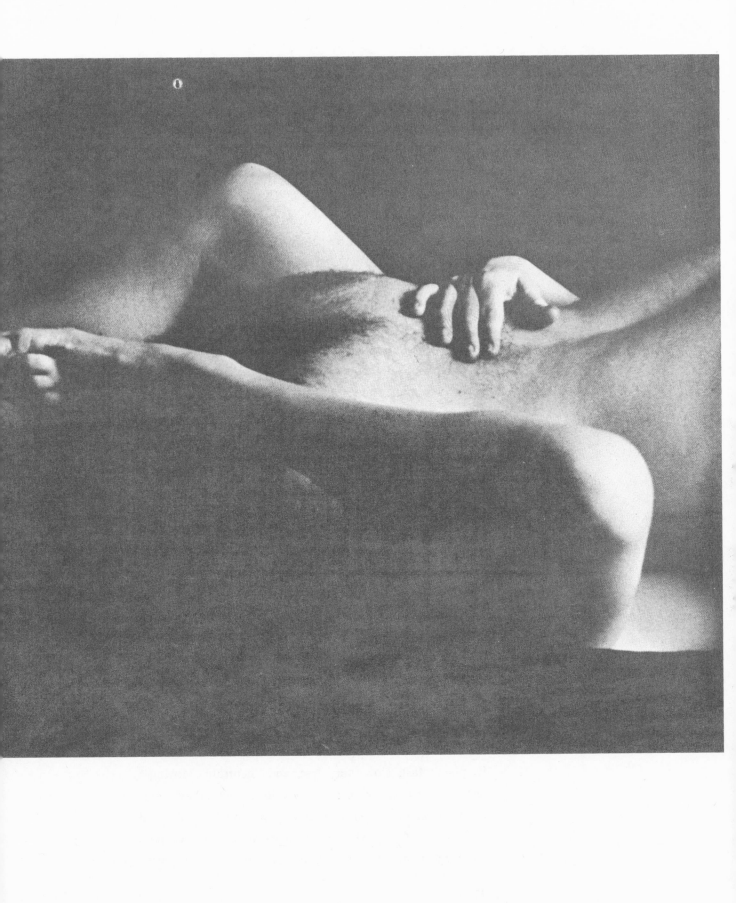

screwing motion with this penis. The woman may also engage in this pattern, swivelling her hips in a sort of a circle so as to create delightful sensations for the penis—and for the vagina, as well. In some positions, the basic in-and-out movement can be varied, in that the penis is in the vagina at a slight angle, pressing harder against one section than against the rest of the vagina.

These movements can be coordinated by the two partners in any of a number of ways. Together, both partners can move in-and-outer, pulling away from each other at the same time Relatively inexperienced men and women should be careful when they do this, in that the penis can draw out of the vagina. Another way is for the man to perform the sexual motions while the woman rests—and then the woman can do this to the man while he relaxes. This can be done in almost any position: there is no reason why the one on top can't rest while the one on bottom moves, for instance, although many couples never think of trying this. Or, one partner can use one type of movement while the other uses another. For example, the woman on her back can use a circular hip rotation while her man drives up and down, in and out of her.

The extent of movement can also be varied. The man will move forward and backward, for the most part, so that he will experience the friction on the head of his penis. But the depth of peneration may vary, even with the same direction of movement being used. He may drive his shaft deep into his woman, or her might make only a shallow penetration. A woman may rotate her hips in a wide, full arc—or she might use a tight little circular movement.

The speed of movement is an important key to variety in intercourse. Basically, there are four speeds, and each has its place: fast, slow, very fast, and "neutral." Moving very fast can be exciting in some positions—those that don't put a strain on either partener and don't involve only shallow penetration. Obviously, very fast movement is not possible when the penis is only slightly inserted. And inexperienced

220

partners should avoid very rapid movement, especially in that coordinating is much more difficult at high speeds. Fast movements are generally more pleasing to the man than to the woman, although most women will crave high-speed sex once in a while. Generally, the slower speed is better for the woman and it is recommended for most of the less basic positions.

And there is "neutral," or no speed at all. You and your woman can simply press against each other after you have achieved penetration—usually deep penetration—and lie there, not moving at all. Many yeople find this very exciting. Some couples do this in a sitting intercourse position, facing each other. In this way, they can look at each other's face and body and talk gently as the excitement builds slowly and steadily—all the way to climax if both partners are patient.

Of course, all the above affects the rhythm of intercourse. But you can also change rhythm without changing speed, direction, or both. Usually, the more even rhythm is best—especially for the woman. But you should experiment with more erratic rhythms, also. In other words, try everything. Make intercourse a new and different experience every time. And changing rhythm is an important part of this. For instance, you can make every stroke even or you can alternate between a hard thrust and a lighter thrust. Or you can thrust in hard and withdraw gently and slowly. You can even add a slight screwing motion to your out-stroke, but drive in straight. Your woman can imitate all the rhythms of a burlesque queen—after all, those bumps and grinds were copied from the bedroom in the first place.

Positions for Sexual Intercourse

Always keep one thing in mind as you read about the various sexual techniques and positions. Successful sex involves experimentation. No man who is to be sexually successful can acquire his expertise from a book or, for that matter, from another's man's advice. You can only acquire so much from someone else's teaching—the rest must come from your own

221

experience and discovery. (It's a good thing that this is true, especially because having sex is more fun than reading about how to have it.) Thus, as you read the descriptions of sexual intercourse positions, always search for new and intriguing variations that you can add to make the act more enjoyable and intriguing and different. Dozens of them exist—you can be sure of that. Merely because the author doesn't put them down on paper in his book doesn't mean that they are not to be used. Far from it. The positions that are listed in this book should be the starting points from which you set out on journeys of sensual exploration. But every little twist of the body, every flex of any muscle group, every press and clinch adds its own little variation.

Every human body is different: the nerve structures have different degrees of sensitivity at different points, the limbs are capable of different degrees of flexibility (obviously, an older person will not be capable of performing many of the techniques outlined here, simply because his limbs are stiff and cannot be made to go into the positions that would be necessary), etc. Thus, what is described is only a bare outline of what you can do. You will have to adapt the various positions to your own needs, desires, and abilities. You and your woman are equipped with arms, legs, vital organs, teeth, tongue, an infinite variety of sensitive areas, etc. In other words, you have all the necessary utensils with which to partake in a feast of sexuality. So, use what you have! Use them all in an infinite variety of positions. Only by casting aside inhibitions and trying all variations will you be able to have explored and discovered the full range of exotic, erotic sensations that belong to dynamic sex. Only by continually experimenting will you begin to learn all there is to be learned about your own sexuality and the body and responses of your woman. Only by continually experimenting will you have made it possible to ward off that killer of successful sex—boredom. It is incredible that so many people have thrown away all hope of ever gaining sexual exhilaration

224

by making too few or too halfhearted attempts—if they attempt at all—at sexual exploration. So, remember that the positions outlined here are only intended as takeoff points for your own personal flight into sexual ecstasy. You can only learn the basic outlines from this book—or any book or any word-of-mouth advice—but the supreme, subtle touches that will make you a master can only be developed by one person: *you*.

Here, then, are the ways you can "swing" with sexual gymnastics, along with assorted variations included in the pictures.

THE WOMAN ON HER BACK POSITIONS

Posture #1 In this particular position, the woman lies flat on her back with her legs somewhat spread and stretched straight out and her hands resting flat. This can be done on a bed, on a couch, or on the floor. Either you or your woman should place a pillow under her buttocks, thus raising her hips slightly and adjusting the angle at which she presents her vagina to your penis. If your woman lies flat, with no pillow under her buttocks, the angle at which her vagina is presented to you will cause some problems in keeping the penis properly and securely inserted. Also, you will not be able to achieve very deep penetration. (If, of course, your penis is too long for your woman's sheath, then this is an advantage of this position, without the use of a pillow.)

In this particular position, the clitoris is exposed to a great deal of stimulation and the penis receives a great deal of stimulating friction in that the vaginal opening is relatively narrow, as compared to some other positions. One effect of having a pillow placed under your woman's buttocks (and you should be sure that it is a thick, well stuffed pollow or, better still, try this with two good-sized pillows) is that your woman is especially likely to be highly stimulated and even drawn to uniquely ecstatic heights because her stomach muscles and the muscles on top of her thighs will be quite tightly stretched. Any woman finds this highly pleasurable.

226

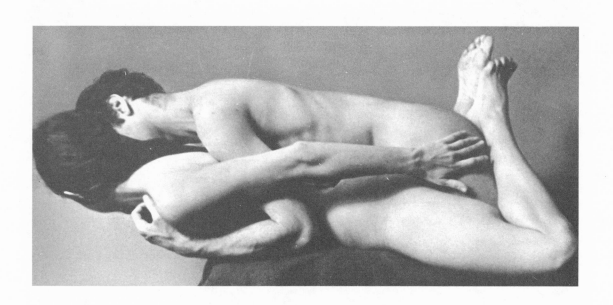

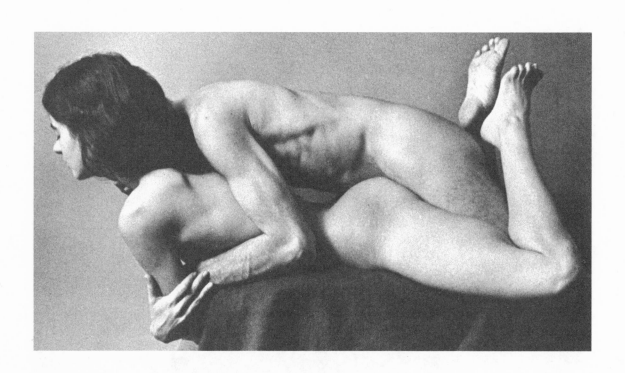

Of course, the placement of your woman is only half of the position. How will you be positioned to enter your woman, when she is in the posture that has just been described?

You are on your hands and knees. Your knees are together, between the thighs of your woman and your hands are flat on the bed (or floor) just above her shoulders or just beside her upper arms. (As a slight variation, some couples enjoy having the man's hands supported on the woman's shoulders, but this may prove tiring for both partners and also may slightly restrict the woman's freedom of movement.) The value of this posture is that you are not putting your weight on your partner's body, which gives her the ability to move rather easily and also to concentrate on the sensations you are causing in her vagina, rather than feeling the more diffused sensations of your body resting on hers. (She is also able to breathe more freely, which is important.) Raised above your woman, as you are, you will be able to see what is going on and you'll be in a position to admire the beautiful body to which you are making love, watching her body move in response to what you are doing to her.

In this position, you will be able to lower your head to kiss your woman on the mouth or face, but—unless you are in excellent condition and are something of an athlete—you will not be able to use only one hand to support your weight and thus have a hand free to caress her body. Your woman, however, will have both hands free to do what she wants. She might grasp your shoulders or your buttocks, so that she can signal you to change your rhythm when she wants. Or she might reach one hand down to your testicles—but she should not do this until she is ready to end the intercourse, in that caressing your testicles during intercourse is almost certain to speed you to a climax.

In this posture, you will be able to use almost any speed and rhythm, except that erratic movements may cause the penis to lose its rather shallow insertion. This can be especially annoying at the point of your climax, when you might tend

229

to become somewhat jerky in your movements—causing you to ejaculate outside your woman, which will lessen your pleasure greatly and disappoint your woman, who will miss the delightful sensations of feeling your penis throbbing within her and of feeling the hot rush of fluid into her vagina. For this reason, you should be sure to control your movements as you reach climax, when you are using this posture.

One final word about this position: especially if you are relatively inexperienced, you may find it awkward to introduce your penis into the vagina (although, the thicker the pillow, the easier it will be). If you have any difficulty making the initial penetration, either you or your woman can guide the penis in by hand. As a man, you may feel embarrassed to have your woman do this, but this feeling of embarrassment is foolish. Many women find it very exciting to grasp a fully erect penis in one hand and pull it into their vagina. So feel free to let your woman help if you have any difficulty.

Posture #2 In this position, the woman assumes the same posture as in the position just described: flat on her back with her legs spread apart somewhat and stretching straight out, her hands resting flat. Once again, one or two thick pillows should be placed under her buttocks.

The difference is that you are on your arms and knees, instead of being on your hands and knees. In this way, your abdomen and chest will be resting on her body, instead of your being raised completely above her. Even still, you should be sure that you keep some of your weight on your arms and knees, so that you are not pressing your full weight against her body. For this position, it is best to be on a bed, rather than on a harder surface, such as the floor. The bed will absorb some of your weight and allow your woman to still have some freedom of motion. If you try this on the floor, your woman may be completely pinned and unable to move—and the weight of your body pressing her to the hard floor is very likely to hurt her, so that she cannot enjoy the intercourse.

234

With your body against your woman's body, her breasts will be caressed, her belly will be stimulated by the motion of your belly, and your lips will be together for all sorts of lip play. Either of you will be able to caress the other's ear with the tongue. And your woman will be able to wrap her arms around you if she wants to hug you closer to her. (This position also makes it easier for her to grasp your buttocks, if she wants. In Posture #1, she has to stretch a bit to do this. Of course, if your body is very long or her arms are very short, this may be impossible in either position.)

Some women will simply never enjoy intercourse in this position, because they will be too bothered by your weight pressing so directly on them—or because they just don't like being so pinned down and unable to move easily. On the other hand, other women get a special pleasure from the feeling of being so completely dominated by a man's body, and they enjoy the stimulation spread out along the full length of their belly and breasts. It is up to you to find out which kind of woman you have. Probably, she will enjoy this posture sometimes and be annoyed by it at other times.

Under any circumstances, you will probably be best off alternating between this posture and some other. For example, you may be up on your hands and knees part of the time and lower yourself onto your arms and knees part of the time. One effect of doing this will be to slightly shift the position of your penis in your woman's vagina—a sensation that will please both of you.

This position is a tiring one for both partners, and there is another reason to switch from it to another position during intercourse. Because of the closeness of your two bodies, you will be somewhat limited in the movements you can make. Rotating motions will be difficult and it will be almost impossible to use very much speed. Despite these limitations, the position is a valuable one for most couples, and you should definitely try it.

235

Posture #3 This position is somewhat similar to Postures #1 and 2, but it is less common. Your woman rests her buttocks on the edge of a low bed, arching her back, her hands gripping the edge of the bed. Her legs are spread apart, slanting down toward the floor, with her knees bent and her calves slanting back toward the bed. Her toes are on the floor and her head and back are flat on the bed. It is important that your woman's buttocks are on the edge of the bed and not hanging over the floor. If the buttocks are too low, the vagina will not be positioned correctly for your entry. It is also best that her legs are spread enough that her buttocks are tightened.

Even more than is the case with Postures #1 and #2, this posture stretches your woman's stomach muscles and the muscles on top of her thighs. With her back arched and her body in a gentle curve toward the floor (with her buttocks on the edge of the bed and her legs folded back under her) her muscles are stretched into a taut instrument that will respond with delight to all stimulation.

You will want to place yourself in the position of resting on your arms and feet. (Your arms will be on the bed and your feet, of course, will be on the floor. In this way, your body will be arched against hers and before intercourse you can glide your body up and down against her skin to stimulate and intrigue her. Because your penis will be entering her vagina at such a sharp angle, her clitoris will be sharply stimulated. The angle at which your penis has made its entry will also have the effect of making your woman feel that her vagina is being stretched by your penis—which will also please her very much. You can expect your woman to encourage you to use this position quite often—perhaps more often than you will want to use it, in that this position may prove quite tiring to you.

Using this posture, you will be able to use a rotating movement in combination with the forward-backward, in-and-out motion. As far as speed and rhythm are concerned, the greatest limitation on you will be in slipping away from your woman

236

if you go too fast—or if the floor on which your feet are resting is particularly slippery. Your woman may want to hold your waist or hips with her hands when you are having intercourse in this posture.

Posture #4 This is a very common position; in fact, it might be called the standard posture of women throughout the world. For many, many couples who think that sexual experimentation is "perverse," this is, indeed, the *only* position. But don't let this make you think that this position is too common to use. While it is foolish to restrict oneself completely to intercourse in this posture, it is just as foolish to disregard this approach entirely.

In this position, the woman lies flat on her back, arms by her side, thighs apart and knees up. (As you can see, the only difference between this posture and the woman's position in Postures #1 and #2 is the fact that the knees are up. Of course, there are dozens of intermediate position variations between the knees-full-up position and the legs-straight-out position.) If you wish, you may place a pillow under her buttocks to permit easier entry for your penis, but the pillow is not as necessary in this posture as in others. The raising of the knees positions the vagina for relatively easy entry; unless the bed is very soft and sags under the woman's buttocks, the pillow is really not needed.

The man kneels between the woman's thighs, resting on his arms and knees—or on his hands and knees. (The choice is similar to the choice between Postures #1 and #2, but you can be less concerned about pressing too heavily on your woman, even if you choose to stay in the lower position —which is, indeed, more popular. If you choose this position, keep your knees together; if they slip apart, your body will rest more heavily on your woman and you may hurt her or dampen her pleasure by restricting her ability to move. Of course, if you are having intercourse on a hard surface, such as the floor, your woman will probably prefer your raising your body on your hands, rather than resting on your arms.)

239

Women like this position because it is comfortable and the woman has complete freedom to use her hands to caress down your back, buttocks, and thighs. If she wishes, your woman may entwine her legs around your thighs or calves, rubbing against your skin to further excite and stimulate you. She, herself, is able to receive many intriguing sensations when your penis is inside her by every subtle movement and flexing of her thighs.

In this position, you will be able to use any kind of sexual movement at any speed or rhythm—and your woman will be free to do the same. You can achieve relatively deep penetration or you can have shallow, titillating peneration by lifting your buttocks away from your woman.

Posture #5   Delight of delights! This position is a favorite of those who use it—although many couples have never thought to try it. It's really quite simple and well worth trying your hand at.

Place your woman spread-eagle on her back, arms apart and thighs spread wide, but with her legs flat on the bed. Again, as with many other positions, you may want to place a pillow under her buttocks. Now, lie over her, supporting yourself on your hands (or arms) and knees, with your thighs close together. After all the preliminaries, introduce your penis into her vagina. Make sure that your organ is inserted as deeply as possible within her. Then, have her bring her thighs together—slowly, so that you don't lose the penetration. She should bring her thighs together as close as she can, so that her ankles are touching each other, her calves touching each other, and her thighs pressing your genitals and each other. As she does this, you will be sliding your knees down away from your body, straightening your legs and allowing them to slide up on top of your woman's legs. You should not separate your own knees in this process. When the two of you have completed this leg movement, your legs will be together on top of her legs, which are also close together. Your genitals will be captured between her thighs. By this point, your penis is tightly held and you will find this an

240

utterly stimulating sensation. Part of your penis will still be in her vagina, which grips your organ tightly as the vaginal walls are pressed together by your woman's legs; part of the shaft of your penis will be gripped—just as tightly —by the soft thighs your woman is pressing together. In this position (often called the "Coital Boomerang"), with your woman's legs close together, you will inevitably find that you are not achieving a particularly deep penetration. As a result of this, you will not be able to use sharp or fast sexual movements. Very subtle movements, based on contracting and relaxing your muscles slowly and steadily, will be appropriate. Despite this limitation, both of you will get great pleasure and extreme excitement from this position. There is also another advantage to this position. Like it or not, there will inevitably be times when your penis is somewhat less than rock-hard. At these times, this position will be found useful in keeping your organ as hard as possible for as long as possible. But the delights of this position are great enough that you shouldn't wait for a soft erection problem before trying this. Even though this position is useful when you lack a completely hard erection, it is even better when you have a full erection to offer.

As in most woman-on-her-back positions, your woman will have her hands free to explore your back and buttocks. At the slow pace that this position requires, these titillating explorations will be especially delightful for both of you.

Posture #6 This position is a variation on Posture #4, but it has its own special twist to it. Have your woman lie on her back—on a bed; this position would not be comfortable on a hard surface. Your woman's thighs should be stretched apart and her knees brought right up almost to her breast—as far as possible without being painful. In this posture, her feet will be above and to the sides of her buttocks, which are fully up off the bed. You should take your position over her, supporting yourself on your hands and knees. Insert your penis as far into her vagina as you can. And make no mistake,

241

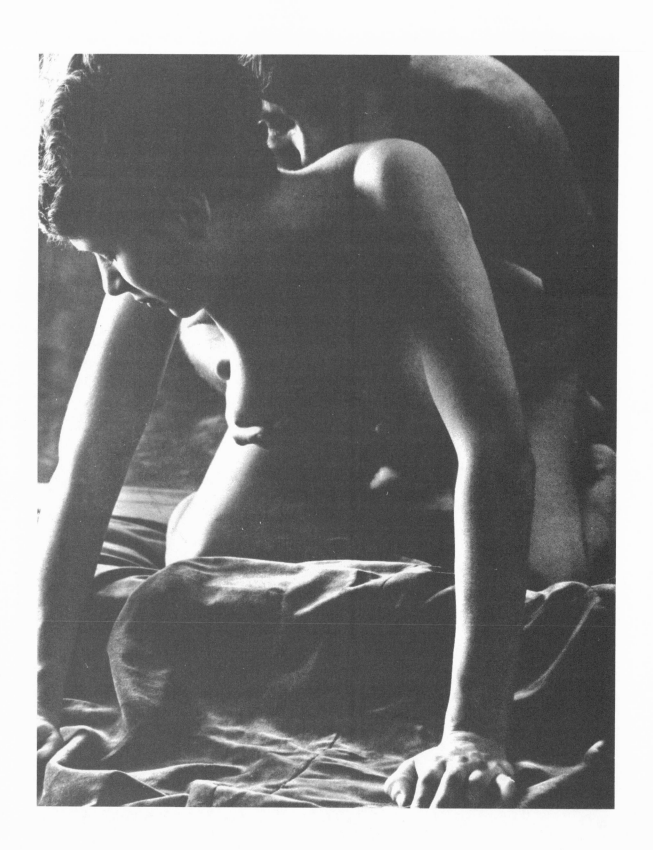

this position allows you to make a very deep penetration as the vaginal opening is drawn as far open as possible, ready for complete conquest by your shaft. Your penis will be going in as far as the uterus and your woman will delight in the myriad of intriguing sensations. (It will seem to your woman that your penis is longer than usual, but what really happens is that this position makes the vaginal canal shorter than usual. At any rate, you should be careful when you thrust in; a sharp and hard thrust may hurt her.)

As the normal position will be for her knees to be perhaps a foot above her breasts, get her to pump her knees up and down slightly as this will have the effect of adding extra stimulation for your penis because of the extra bit of friction that is caused. This will produce a particularly nice feeling for her, too.

Almost any rhythm, speed, and pattern of sexual movements will be possible in this position, with the exception that you have to be careful not to jab too hard if this causes your woman pain. And make sure that your woman does not have any irritations within her vagina, as this will be a rather painful position for her if she does have any.

Posture #7 Again, have your woman lie on her back, either on a bed or couch or on the floor. But this time, have her raise her legs straight up, encircling your hips and locked together behind you at her ankles. You, of course, will be on your arms and knees. In this position, you will be very close and you may find that your sexual movements are somewhat limited. You will probably not be able to go very fast—but this position is so intimate that you shouldn't really want to. Also, the two of you will not be able to use contrasting movements, because of the tightly locked relationship of your bodies. This, however, is not a disadvantage; it is the basis of one important value of this posture: it is quite useful for a young, inexperienced woman as this position will teach her how to coordinate her movements with yours. In this position, she will be able to feel your tempo and thus pick up the

244

technique quite quickly. You will be physically guiding her, just as if you were dancing and leading her with a firm hand on the small of her back. The movements of your hips will control the movements of her legs—and, just as the old song says, the thigh bone is connected to the hip bone—and her hips will imitate the sexual movements of hers.

Many experienced couples enjoy this position—even though they have no need of teaching or learning co-ordination. They simply enjoy the physical sensations of having their bodies so fully and closely intertwined. Beyond this, the woman enjoys the pshchological pleasure of feeling that she has engulfed her man—and the man enjoys this sense of having been so completely swallowed up in the body of his woman.

Posture #8 This is a slight variation on Posture #7. Instead of wrapping her legs around your hips, your woman wraps them around your legs. Her ankles do not lock together in this position. Rather, each ankle locks onto the inner top of your calf. In this way, your pelvic regions are not so tightly pressed together, and you will have somewhat greater freedom of sexual movement—even though you will still be more restricted than in most other positions. You will still be on your arms and knees, but you will be more able to lift your body away from your woman's body, relieving some of the pressure on her.

If you are just beginning to try using contrasting movements (for instance, with you moving up and down while your woman rotates her hips), this position will allow you to try this without completely losing all sense of co-ordination.

Posture #9 Again, this is yet another variation on Posture #7.
Instead of having her legs pointing straight up, as in the first stage of Posture #7, your woman bends her knees. Thus, instead of clasping your body at the hips (or at the calves, as in Posture #8), your woman's legs will clasp you by your chest or neck. You should be on your hands and knees in

245

this position. In most woman-on-her-back positions, the suppleness and athletic condition of the woman is not of really paramount importance. But in this position it *is* of importance. The more supple or athletic woman will be able to wrap her legs around your neck and still have much ability to move with great freedom. The less supple woman may have to restrict herself to clasping your chest—and her ability to do various sexual movements may also be restricted. Nonetheless, this position will prove very enjoyable. It must be said, however, that the increased freedom of sexual movement that a suppler, more athletic woman brings to this position can help create a wild, passionate session of truly delightful sensations. This position is the favorite of many couples—especially more athletic couples!

One of the more interesting aspects of this position is the ease with which it can be alternated with variation-positions —Postures #10 and #11, described below—for a most exciting session of intercourse.

Posture #10   From Posture #9, you can roll into Posture #10. Have your wife roll her hips over to either her right or left side, still keeping you clenched between her thighs. While you will be partially following this change of posture, your knees will still be on the bed or ground, so that your body will be slightly twisted. You will feel a slightly different feeling in this new position, because your penis will be lodged slightly differently within your woman vagina's. If your woman is rather plump, she will find this position rather more restful.

Posture #11   In this position, the woman lies on her back, with her legs pointing straight up—as in Posture #7. The man's position, however, is very different from the arms and knees posture of #7. Instead, the man is erect on his knees, his body straight up, parallel to the woman's upraised legs and perpendicular to the woman's body. Rather than lying over your woman's body, you are kneeling at the altar of her sexuality.

247

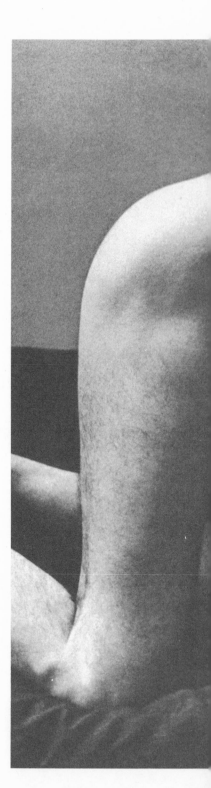

There are several approaches to her body, depending on such factors as your height and the length of her legs. She might wrap her legs around your neck or hook her heels over your shoulders. Or you might hold her legs or feet with your hands. Under any circumstances, you will probably find this position somewhat easier to use if there is a pillow under your woman.

Some couples begin intercourse in this position, but most find it preferable to move into this postiion from Posture #9.

You will have a great deal of freedom in this position, so thae you can move fast or slowly, using an in-and-out motion or a circular screwing motion, or any combination. You will be in position to feast your eyes upon the entire lovely form of your woman—and you'll be able to view the motion of your penis in and out of her vagina.

The fact that you and your woman are not in very much bodily contact with each other recommends this position at times when the summer is in full steam and more conventional couples think it's "too darn hot."

Posture #12   In this postition, your wife is on her back, with her right leg bent at the knee and her left leg is pulled up sharply at the knee but bent over and lying on its side. The vagina is widely opened in this position and with her left leg drawn up sharply on its side, the way it is, your woman is vulnerable to great pleasure. Drive home your advantage!

For yourself, you can use almost any basic position. Just make sure your woman keeps that left knee bunched up tight against her side and flat on the bed. (In that you will probably be ramming hard into your woman in this position, she probably will not enjoy using this position on a hard surface, so you had better stay on the bed or sofa for this one.) If your woman finds it easier, she can grasp her left knee with her left hand, to be sure that it stays bunched up tightly.

If you feel like experimenting—and why shouldn't you?—

250

you might try approaching your partner with your right leg bent sharply at the knee (heel touching buttock), left leg stretched out and body supported by your elbows. Get right in there and make your entrance.

Because this position widens the vagina, you may find more pleasure in using a circular, screwing motion instead of the simple in-and-out movement. You can also shift your body somewhat from left to right, to keep shifting the angle of your penis within the vagina. Generally speaking, these kinds of movements are especially valuable in any position that widens the vagina, in that such movements take fullest advantage of the increased accessibility of the various areas of the vaginal walls.

A vigorous motion is also worth trying in this position, although slower movements are certainly possible and will almost always please almost any woman.

Posture #13   Have your woman lie on her back, with a pillow beneath her buttocks or lower back. Her right leg is in the conventional position and bent at the knee. Her left leg is drawn straight back toward her, bent quite sharply at the knee—almost giving the impression that your woman is making a very energetic kick with her left foot.

There is nothing especially unique about this posture; it is just a variation that can be used to add a little variety.

You can approach your woman in any one of the usual positions. If you want, you can have her wrap her left foot partially around your body or neck. Or, if you shift most of your weight to your left knee and arm (or hand), you can free your right hand to titillate your woman's clitoris or anus while you are inserted within her—either not moving or moving slowly and gently.

8

Sexual
Intercourse
Positions:
part two

The man on his
back positions

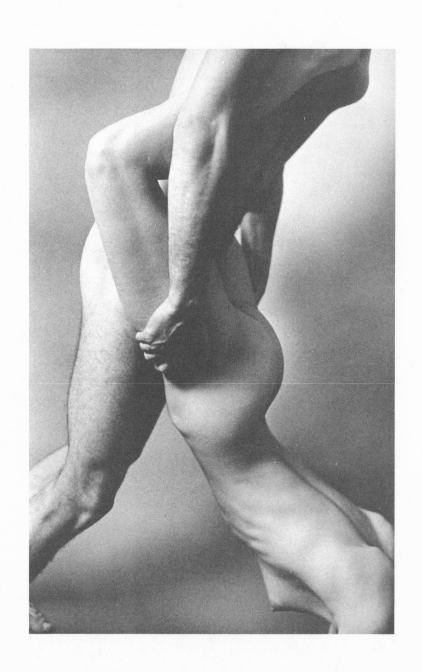

ALL of the positions described in Chapter 7 involved the woman lying on her back with the man above her. Many couples make it through life without ever trying more than two or three of the thirteen suggested woman-on-her-back positions. An even greater number of couples never try *any* position in which the woman is not on her back and the man above her. How foolish it is for couples to ignore the many positions in which the woman is not on her back!

There is nothing at all perverse or "abnormal" about experimenting with postures of different sorts. And it is generally much better to do this kind of experimenting than to allow sex to become boring.

THE MAN ON HIS BACK POSITIONS

This is the set of positions that has been traditionally looked down upon by many tribes. The reason for this attitude, of course, is that the woman being over the man is thought to symbolize the dominance of women over men. You are quite welcome to read any symbolic meaning into a sexual intercourse position such as any position where the woman is above the man—but you should realize that this is just your personal opinion, molded by your anxieties, fears, insecurities, and doubts. If this is your view—if you have a strong distaste for intercourse positions in which your woman is over you— then, naturally, you should not try to hide from your own feelings or try to repress your own sensibilities. There is no point to trying to enjoy the act of sexual union in any position that—for any reason—makes it impossible for you to enjoy sex. There is no point to trying it, only to spoil everything for your wife or to spend days and weeks afterward hating yourself or being disgusted with the very idea of sex.

If you have this kind of attitude about the man-on-his-back positions, then it is up to you to decide whether or not you want to try to change the way you feel about such postures. Remember, it is your own personal taste involved in this: there is nothing actually wrong with having intercourse with the woman astride. Such a posture may symbolize female dominance *in your eyes,* but, in reality, this kind of position is quite legitimate and is one of the tools of successful sex. You may or may not be able to overcome your inhibitions, but you should remember that sexual power is largely based on the abandonment of inhibitions.

After all, if the man-on-his-back positions really made the woman dominant, then you would be trapped in this position —just as the woman is often trapped in intercourse positions in which the man is on top of her. But, of course, you are not. You can roll over and assume the top position any time you choose.

Now, it may be the case that you have nothing against these positions, but your woman feels that being on top of you degrades your masculinity. If your woman has any such inhibitions about these positions, you should carefully explain these matters to her. For one thing, male dominance should mean that your woman does what you want her to do —and this includes climbing on top when you want her to climb on top.

Some of these positions are rather difficult for the woman, simply because they are awkward, and before long her muscles will feel like bursting asunder. Not exactly a favorable sign for satisfying sex! She will then be strongly inclined to favor those positions in which she is most comfortable. Well, she

may be assuming the "dominant" role in terms of being physically on top, but this is the time for you to show her who is *really* in control, who is really the master of the relationship. Insist that she favor you with the positions that intrigue you —and if she starts to whine about her aching bones before she has adequately explored and developed a certain position, then give her a good slap where she's built for slapping and tell her to get on with what you want her to be doing.

If you are a young husband, remember this: never tolerate muscular softness in your wife. And if she feels her limbs aching as soon as she starts being really active in sexual play, then you should realize that this is a very clear indication to you that she is leading too easy a life and is not working hard enough. Certainly, if your woman refuses to get on top because she thinks sex is only good when she can lie on her back like a pork chop, you should see to it that she learns to play the part you want her to play in bed. If, for one reason or another, her laziness is interfering with your pleasure, it is up to you to correct the situation—and fast!

So far, in dealing with the man-on-his-back positions, we have stressed the advantages of making use of variety. And this is very important—in fact, more essential than anything else. However, there are some other factors that you might wish to consider. Keep them in mind when you are choosing positions for intercourse.

Aside from the variety it offers, the man-on-his-back position is useful in that it allows you, the man, to rest yourself. It requires very little effort on your part, allowing you to take it easy while preparing yourself for greater things to come. It is also quite valuable at times when you are too fatigued to play a very active, energetic role—after a rough day at work or after a couple rounds of vigorous man-on-top sexual intercourse—but when the two of you still want to have a go at it (or *another* go at it).

The man-on-his-back positions (or, some of them, at least) are good if you or your woman are especially fat.

257

There are other, more important, advantages, too.

First of all, if your woman is rather inexperienced and is, perhaps, handicapped by the possession of a certain sense of modesty and sexual uncertainty, placing her in a position of physical authority over you is likely to help break down this mental hesitation or Victorian modesty. Any one of these postures will give her substantial encouragement to thoroughly explore you and to build up her own sexual self-confidence. Lying beneath you, she can feel that you are doing things to her—rather than with her—and she can mentally hide from her own sexuality and sex drives. Having her on top will expose her sex drives to her. Unless she just sits there—and no woman with a man's penis in her vagina is going to just sit there—she will have to assert herself sexually, overcoming all hesitations and all modesty.

Secondly, when the woman is on top, she sets her own pace and controls the intensity of her own genital stimulation. In this way, the two of you can learn what speed and pace will best suit her. This posture (woman astride, in any variation) will let your woman probe for herself so that she can discover what suits her best in the way of vaginal stimulation. And, as she learns what is best for her, you will learn what is best for her. (On the other hand, if your woman is rather experienced in sexual matters, this posture will permit her to show you precisely what she would like you to do.) Naturally, the first step toward bringing full sexual satisfaction to your partner is the learning of how to control your natural instinct toward a quick climax. But it is equally important— even though this could only come after a degree of climax control has been gained—for both of you to discover how your woman can be drawn out toward full sexual stimulation, complete sexual satisfaction, and total ecstasy.

There is another value of the man-on-his-back positions and this one value is more important than all the others, combined. Your woman, being on top, guides the movement and speed to suit her needs and she can pretty much control the direction of the penis in her vagina—to hit "just that spot"—so that she can usually reach orgasm much more quickly than in other positions. And, because you can remain reasonably relaxed in these positions, without using much energy on the sexual movements involved, you can direct a concentrated effort toward holding off your climax until your woman has reached hers—or is just ready to reach hers. Furthermore, the physical relationship of the genitals in these positions aids the woman in her drive toward orgasm while aiding you in your efforts to delay your orgasm. So long as she keeps her genitals pressed down on your body, your penis should receive barely any friction at all. If she slides down along your body until the top of your penis presses firmly against her clitoris, she can receive enormous stimulation without in any way hastening you toward your climax. All the usual motions—side-to-side movements, rocking motions, rotary hip twirling, circular screwing, et cetera—will accomplish this very well indeed. If your woman sticks to these essential movements and lets you, at the same time, move in and out as much as you want, then she can receive the highly intense stimulation she needs—without bringing you over the brink too soon.

Don't think it is cheating to take advantage of these ways of postponing your climax while hastening hers. There is no reason at all not to utilize these valuable aspects of the man-on-his-back positions. They are some of Nature's devices to give you a chance to offset the natural difference in timing between men and women in the sexual pressure cooker.

Yet another advantage of these positions—although a marginal advantage—is that it is possible to have intercourse even when you are not completely erect. And if you reach orgasm too soon and lose the full size and stiffness of your erection, your woman can still keep going. Even if you reached your climax in some other position, you can switch to a man-on-his-back posture so that your woman can make her way to her orgasm. Of course, your woman will be aware of the smaller,

softer stance of your penis, but she will still be able to receive some pleasure from it in these positions.

With all the positions that involve you, the man, lying on your back, with your woman astride you, it is especially important to remember that you should engage in sufficient sex play beforehand, thoroughly arousing your woman. The reason for this is that deep penetration is often very difficult and if it can be achieved very often it will cause a certain amount of pain unless her vagina is quite thoroughly lubricated. For this reason, many couples enjoy starting out in a woman-on-her-back position—preferably a rather basic one—and then rolling over into a man-on-the-back posture. In this way, you can be fully sure that the vaginal lubrication is sufficient before beginning the use of a woman-on-top position. There are really only two basic positions in which the man can lie—although there are also slight variations on these. (Both postures, interestingly enough, are nameless; so socially unacceptable was it to use them—or, at least, to openly admit using them—that nobody ever saw fit to give them names. Of course, if you are one of those people who feel that every sexual posture should have its own special label, then you are welcome to create whatever names you want to give them.) To assume a position for intercourse with your woman astride you, lie on your back (on the floor or on a bed) either with your thighs pressed together or with your thighs apart, with approximately twenty-four inches separating your ankles. These are the two basic postures the man may assume, but there are variations on each. With your thighs apart, you can either have your legs flat on the floor (or bed) or you can bend them slightly at the knees. Which you choose makes a great difference in the angle of insertion. With your thighs together, you will probably find it better to keep your knees unbent (or only very slightly bent), but you can vary this posture by placing one or two thick, well stuffed pillows under your buttocks.

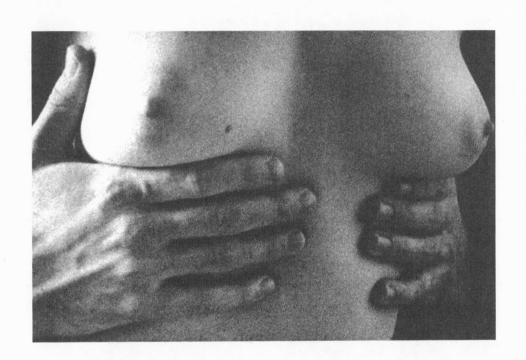

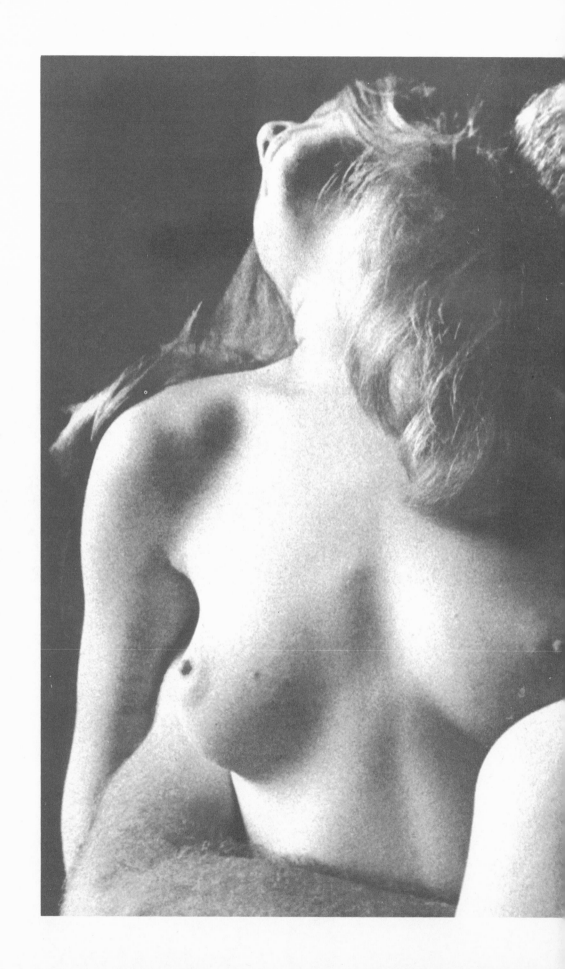

Posture #14 The man is lying on his back, thighs together. The woman crouches over him, on her hands and knees, almost in an attitude of prayer. Her thighs are, of course, apart and her knees are on either side of her man's hips. A reasonably deep penetration is permitted here and this is a position that is quite easy for almost any woman to manage. The woman can raise and lower her head and use her hands to good advantage. She is in a comfortable position to teasingly introduce the penis only slightly into her vagina or to hold the man's part with one hand and manipulate it against her clitoris and vaginal lips. When she is sufficiently wet and ready to accept the penis, she can lower herself completely onto it. By shifting her hips in either a "bump" or "grind" fashion, she can alter the angle at which the penis is in her vagina.

The woman can set her own pace in this position, moving very, very slowly or slamming away very fast. She can use either a straight up-and-down motion or a circular, screwing movement. And she can alter her rhythm to suit her sexual needs.

The man can raise his knees, hips, or both to achieve greater stimulation. He can make a bridge from his shoulders to his heels, if he wants, but most men cannot keep this up for very long. He can lie reasonably still, but will probably get more pleasure by moving his pelvic area in rhythm with his woman's rhythm. Either an up-and-down or side-to-side movement is possible, and a circular, screwing motion is particularly useful. By and large, all these movements will be restricted somewhat by the position and by the movements of the woman, but the restricted motions that are possible for the man are still pleasurable for both partners.

The first time you try this position—especially if you have, in the past, only had intercourse in the man-above positions—you will be pleasantly surprised to find that your hands are free to do many different things. You may play with, or caress, your woman's breasts, belly, or sides. You may reach around to hold her buttocks. Or you can grasp her by the hips to guide her movements. You can let her rest her breasts and chest on your hands, or grasp her under the arms—in either case supporting her upper body.

Posture #15   This position is quite similar to Posture #14. Now, however, your woman supports herself on her knees and hands *with her elbows unbent*. Thus, her trunk will be raised higher above you—which, in turn, lowers her buttocks. This will give you even more freedom with your hands and open up your view of the genital contact. More important, this is a particularly restful position for the woman because of the crouch in which she has placed herself. At the same time, she is allowed a great deal of choice in how she wishes to move her hips, although *your* freedom of movement is not improved.

Posture #16   This, actually, is a series of variations of the woman stretched out over the man and, of course, is identical to the positions taken by the man in many of the postures when the woman is on *her* back. With the man on *his* back, the woman may have her thighs separated or together (at some point during the intercourse) and she can be supporting herself on her hands or elbows. Thus, she has an infinite variety of positions at her disposal. Depending on how far her breasts are from the man (in other words, whether she is supporting herself on her hands or by her arms) she is able to receive a full caressing treatment from you by hand or by mouth. Being in this position, your only freedom of action will be to reach where you can with your hands to stimulate her and, of course, to play with her breasts, either with your hands or with your mouth.

At any rate, if you choose to engage in intercourse in the general position of woman above, man lying on his back, you should insist that your wife make full use of these assorted nuances in placing herself *full length* over you. And you should not be embarrassed to place your body in the "female"

267

position—thighs apart and knees bent—while your wife drops from her posture on her knees to a more stretched-out posture between your legs. Of course, in many of these variations, penetration will not remain deep, but your woman can slide from posture variation to posture variation to give the two of you a variety of intriguing sensations.

Posture #17   In this position, your woman is squatting over you, supporting herself on her knees, but sitting erect, with her vagina directly over your erect penis. In this posture, she lowers her body onto yours, impaling herself on your erection. In this kneeling posture, your woman has a great deal of freedom of movement, so that she can twist her hips in a very wide arc and raise them up and down. The up-and-down movement is restricted only by the necessity of retaining your penis within her, so, if you use an up-and-down movement in coordination with hers—pressing your pelvis up while she lifts her hips and lowering your pelvis (pressing your buttocks hard into the bed) when she moves her hips downward—the total movement of her hips can be quite large and vigorous.

To get full value out of this position, both of you will have to be relatively experienced and able to coordinate your movements perfectly. If you can do this, you will be able to use great speed and energy in this posture. Of course, if you are less experienced, you will have to go more slowly, but you will still get great pleasure from this delightful position.

Posture #18   This posture is the same as Posture #17, except that your woman squats over you, supporting herself on her heels, rather than resting on her knees. Instead of kneeling erect over you, she is squatting back on her heels, and her torso may slant very slightly backwards. This position soon becomes rather uncomfortable for the woman, so this is a very short-term posture. Your woman will almost certainly prefer the comfort and freedom of movement of Posture #17 to the discomfort of this position—and, as a result, she will undoubtedly do more for you in the former posture.

The position of squatting on the heels has little to recommend it (for most couples), and it is included here just to suggest one more way of achieving variety. Of course, none of this means that you might not be one of those rare couples who really favor this generally unpopular posture. And, if you are such a couple, then why care what others think of this position? So give this posture a try. You may be the ones who really like it.

Posture #19 This is also a difficult position and not particularly useful, but it, too, can be tried for variety.

Here, your woman will place herself over you, supporting herself on her two feet and two hands at such a height that her vagina is just over your penis. As you might guess, this is a very short-term position, because of the discomfort it will cause your woman. But there is another problem encountered in using this position: Your penis will be aiming in a rather different direction in relation to the vagina than in more basic positions. As a result of this, once union is achieved, you must both be very careful that you don't become disengaged. (Relatively inexperienced or overly excitable couples will most certainly lose the connection in this posture.)

Unless your woman has the muscle build and overall strength of an Amazon, the only movement possible in this position is a circular, screwing movement, used in a slow, steady rhythm.

Posture #20 Here is a rather complex variation on the basic man-on-his-back positions. As usual, you are lying on your back, preferably with your thighs somewhat apart. Instead of crouching, kneeling, or squatting over you, your woman lies down on top of you—*on her back* and *in the opposite direction*. In other words, her legs rest on your shoulders and her head is between your legs—but she is facing *up*.

You then raise your upper torso and, at the same time, your woman reaches her hands around your neck, grasping them

270

together behind your head. At this stage of the development of this position, all four arms are making contact with one or the other of her legs.

Now you insert your penis and, by rocking back and forth, the penetration is completed and the necessary friction is created. For good reason, this posture is often called the "Sexual Shock."

Of all the man-on-his-back positions, this is among the least effective in delaying the male orgasm. But, after all, that isn't the only function of these positions. And, while this posture may not slow your orgasm, it is likely to speed hers.

Posture #21 Here is a position that your woman might hesitate about using, but it is very stimulating and you should just lay down the law and tell her to do what you say. You are on your back and she sits down on top of your penis—supporting herself on her hands and knees—facing away from you. She will have great freedom of movement and can use a vigorous up-and-down motion or almost any other movement she feels like using. One disadvantage of this position, from the woman's standpoint, is that her clitoris is not stimulated as it is in most other woman-on-top positions. Also, she may object to facing away from you during intercourse, which may strike her as too mechanical and impersonal. A third disadvantage is that you will not be able to caress her breasts or belly in this position. (On the other hand, you will be able to caress her buttocks quite easily.)

One reason that this position is worth trying, despite its drawbacks—and aside from the fact that it offers a bit of interesting variety—is that the penis is in the vagina in a way that is different from the other positions that have been described above. The underside of the penis, which is vulnerable to great stimulation, is pressing against the front of the vagina and is stimulated by the woman's pelvic bone while the head of the penis is receiving a great deal of stimulation deeper within the vagina.

271

If you bend your knees and draw your legs up, you can press your woman's sides between your thighs while having intercourse in this position.

Posture #22 This position is an interesting and rewarding variation on Posture #21.

Instead of supporting her torso on her hands, your woman drops down to rest on her forearms or to actually rest her breasts and face on your ankles or on the bed between your feet. This is a reasonably comfortable position for her, although she may find that her freedom of movement is slightly limited. Her buttocks will now be completely accessible to your hands and you may even choose to titillate her anus with one of your fingers.

Like Posture #21, this position is especially good for the man, who is sure to receive new and intriguing sensations.

Posture #23 This position is of little value except for variety and for a bit of fun that doesn't involve high sexual stimulation. You lie on your back with your knees bent slightly and your thighs together. Then, your woman sits squarely on you—rather than supporting herself on her knees or feet or whatever. In this position, your woman is resting her full weight on your pelvic area and her buttocks come to rest solidly on you. If she is a hefty girl, you will have no freedom of movement at all. And, because she is sitting down, she has no independent means of supporting herself or moving appreciably. The only friction, therefore, will have to result from a certain twisting or squirming of the woman's body and other secondary stimulation, such as genital twitching or other muscle contraction and relaxation by either partner.

Posture #24 This final man-on-his-back position is reserved for couples in which the woman is muscular, strong, and used to hard work —in other words, a thoroughly fine physical specimen with highly developed muscles and muscle control. (If you happen to be married to an Olympic swimming champion or Rosie the Riveter, this position is for you.)

Have your woman lie down on top of you, in the opposite direction and facing downward. Her feet will be placed, toes down, on either side of your head and she will be supporting herself over you with her powerful arms.

To get the necessary up-and-down, up-and-down, in-and-out friction, all she needs to do is lower and raise her body by bending and straightening her arms. In other words, she has to do the old push-up arm bends you probably were forced to do during gymnasium period in school. And—as you probably remember—it's tough work! So, you had better be sure that your woman has the strength and stamina to perform this technique. Be careful: a woman who is eager to please you, yet who is lacking in the necessary muscle power or stamina might give you an unpleasant shock by suddenly collapsing on you. Don't laugh—it's happened before.

If your woman prefers, of course, she can rest herself between these vigorous up-and-down motions by simply lying prone on your body and relieving the strain on her arm muscles.

All right now, you have read enough about the various man-on-his-back positions and the variations. If you haven't tried any of these positions already, take your woman and try one one or two of them now for yourself.

9

Sexual Intercourse Positions: part three

The standing
positions

THE inexperienced man or woman might think that the twenty-four woman-on-her-back and man-on-his-back postures represent enough variety for anybody. But there is no such thing as enough variety when it comes to sex. And several of the very best positions are yet to come. So, keep on reading and keep on experimenting. You may not even have yet discovered the position that will turn out to be your very favorite. Even if you and your woman are both sexually experienced, there are probably many positions you haven't yet tried—including some you'll wish you had always known about.

THE STANDING POSITIONS

Having intercourse in a standing position is not the most comfortable experience in the world, but there will be times when you'll want to try it. At first, it may seem too difficult, but it is well worth the effort it may take to get the gist of it—and then, after the first time you succeed, you will find it relatively easy to accomplish.

Posture #25 You and your woman stand facing each other. You may both be naked, or you may still have some clothes on but your genitals are exposed to each other.

This position can be used if the two of you are not too far apart in height. For obvious reasons, a man who is six foot five and a woman who is five feet tall will not be able to use this posture.

279

The man bends his knees slightly—just as much as is needed to lower his penis into position below the vaginal opening. The woman stands with her legs apart, her thighs against the outer sides of the man's legs. Pressing their bodies together and supporting each other, the man and woman maneuver until the penis is pressing upward into the vagina. Then, assuming that the vagina is properly lubricated, the woman slides gently down onto the penis. Once penetration is accomplished, the man can straighten up somewhat, as can the woman.

Limited freedom of sexual movement is permitted in this position, but it is possible to create enough genital friction through subtle movement. And—especially if both of you are naked—the pressure of torso against torso, accompanied by passionate deep mouth kissing (which is easy in this position), adds a great deal of excitement.

Posture #26 In Posture #25, the woman's feet remain on the ground. But, if the woman is small enough or the man is strong enough, the man can support the woman's body on his upper legs, so that only the man has his feet on the floor. The direction in which the penis enters the vagina is better in this position than when the woman is standing.

Many couples use this position (or Posture #25) in the shower, but this is, of course, very dangerous. So, try it— but try it on a dry floor.

THE SITTING POSITIONS

Obviously, given the anatomical construction of the male and female human bodies, the man will always be beneath his woman in sitting-position intercourse. (Why is it, one might wonder, that the very same men who shudder with horror at the thought of engaging in woman-astride intercourse, will have no hesitation about trying the sitting positions—in which, of course, the man is underneath and the woman is still astride?)

283

All in all, the sitting positions are far from ideal, because it is often difficult to reach orgasms this way. There are severe limitations on the speed and nature of sexual movements in sitting positions, and it is usually difficult to achieve really intriguing rhythms.

Nonetheless, there are values to these positions, and these values are well worth considering. First, you and your woman are in very close and intimate contact, so that you can hold each other tightly, kiss each other, embrace, and fondle each other. You may feel that these pleasures do not balance off the loss of ability to carry on violent, intriguing, vigorous movements—but there is a time and place for everything, including the characteristics, plusses and minuses of the sitting position.

More important in the way of an advantage of these postures is the fact that they can be used in places not otherwise convenient for intercourse, such as automobile front seats, etc. (Albeit, automobiles are less comfortable places to make love than beds, but successful marriages are based on keeping sex lively and spontaneous—and "making out" in the front seat of a parked car is excellent for adding the spice of variety to an otherwise comfortable—but somewhat boring—sexual relationship.)

After all, if all you care about is comfort, you can't hope to be a really exciting—and excited—lover.

Posture #27 This position is very easy to understand. You merely sit on the ground with your legs together, stretched right out in front of you, and you lean back slightly, supporting yourself on your hands. (Your hands, of course, are flat on the floor, palms down, to the sides of—and behind—your buttocks.)

Now, how will your wife approach you? Probably the best way is for her to position her vagina directly over your erection while supporting herself with her hands and legs. (Try to visualize this.) Her knees are bent, her arms are unbent, with her hands on the floor on either side of your hips, and her torso dangles over your penis.

285

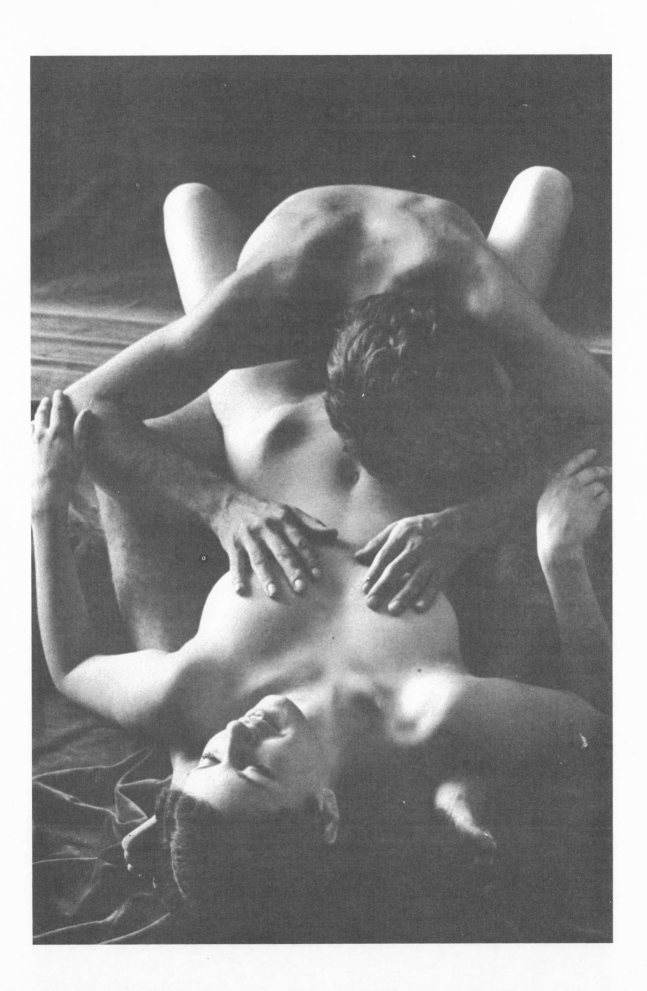

As you will undoubtedly notice, this posture is similar to several of the man-on-his-back postures, except that your back is off the floor and your hands are not free to caress your woman.

Posture #28 This is quite similar to Posture #27, above, except that your knees are folded underneath your thighs. Also, most likely, your body will be arched just a little bit further back than in Posture #27. Your torso is still supported, quite naturally, by your arms, although your hands will probably be placed further back and further out from your body. The farther back you lean, the deeper penetration you will be able to make.

Your woman squats over your penis, sitting on her knees, with the backs of her heels touching her buttocks and her thighs. Of course, her knees are outside of yours.

Posture #29 Here, the man assumes the same position as in Posture #28. Instead of kneeling, the woman squats on her heels, her knees together and her feet about twenty-four inches apart. Her trunk should be slightly bent over, being supported by her arms resting on her knees.

Posture #30 Again, the man assumes the same position as in Posture #28. Rather than kneeling or squatting, the woman sits on the man's lap. This is a very pleasant position because of the great amount of contact of skin against skin. On the other hand, there is the rather serious disadvantage that the woman's freedom to move up and down on your penis is severely restricted.

Posture #31 This is yet another variation in which the man assumes the position desribed in Posture #28. But the woman's position is radically different.

Delight of delights! Your woman can support herself by hanging her ankles around your neck and holding herself up with her arms. This rather wild posture will be quite pleasurable

288

to both of you. But be warned! Be sure that your woman has muscles in her arms—muscles strong enough to support her full weight securely. If she does not and she is ambitious to please you, she might get herself placed in this position and then, without any warning whatsoever, suddenly collapse on top of you. The author is sure that it is totally unnecessary for him to deal at any length with the potential unpleasantries involved in such a catastrophe!

As a matter of fact, it would be well for you to keep in mind, throughout all of your experimenting, that human beings have physical limits and going beyond these limits is simply not worth it. Variety is necessary. Acrobatics and tests of endurance are definitely not necessary.

Posture #32   This is a variation of Posture #31. It will be of value to couples who shun—or are just not up to—the extreme stresses involved in Posture #31. This variation is designed to give your woman a bit more support and take some of the strain off her arms.

Instead of having both of her ankles around your neck, she supports herself by keeping only one leg up in that position while the other limb is placed firmly on the floor or bed to support her. Naturally, she still must maintain her self in position by keeping her arms stretched out straight.

Although this position can be viewed as an easy version of Posture #31, there is a special bonus for couples who are capable of achieving both postures comfortably: the difference in placement of one of your woman's legs cause a difference in the placement of the penis within the vagina. As a result, the two postures provide significantly different sets of intriguing sensations.

Posture #33   In all the five postures described above, from Posture #28 through Posture #32, the man assumed the same position. Knees folded under the thighs with torso arched back, the man supports himself on his hands. Now, here is a variation in the man's position. The man can have something (pillows, a bolster, a sofa back—almost anything that feels comfortable to the back) placed just behind the back, so that this supports his torso instead of the arms carrying that burden. This will give the man greater comfort—permitting a longer, more relaxed, and more enjoyable session of intercourse. It also serves to free the man's hands for all the roaming, caressing, and playing that he may want to do.

Also, in this way, you can see how the various sitting positions can be adapted to the more unorthodox locations for intercourse, such as an automobile front seat, etc. Who says you need a bed for the favorite bedtime sport?

Posture #34 For this position, lean back, supporting yourself with your outstretched arms (unbent at the elbows), and fold your knees up so that they are pointing toward the ceiling. In this position, you can have your woman approach you with any of the postures described above. Or, if you like, you can bend your knees, while still supporting your trunk in the usual fashion, as you separate your thighs.

Posture #35 Here is an interesting way to use a high-backed sofa to attain a position that is a cross between the usual sitting position and some of the more common man-on-his-back positions. Stiffen your body somewhat and stretch out at a forty-five degree angle to the ground. The back of your neck should be resting on the top of the sofa back; your buttocks—tightened —should be supported on the edge of the sofa; and your heels should be on the floor. You can get further support by planting your arms firmly on the sofa on either side of your buttocks.

Your woman can approach in any of a number of ways. She can kneel on the edge of the sofa, facing you, grasping your sides with her hands for extra stability. Or she can use almost any of the other standard postures for women in the various sitting positions.

290

Posture #36   Here, you sit on a stool or chair (or piano bench or whatever is around). Your woman sits on your knees, facing you. You should be leaning back somewhat, to make your penis more accessible to her. The more erect your body is, the less deeply will you be able to achieve penetration.

In order to make this position work, you should make sure that the stool or chair (or whatever it is) on which you are sitting is quite high, so that her feet do not touch the floor. Then, you will joggle your body in order to promote the necessary friction.

Posture #37   Generally speaking, you will not reach great heights of ecstasy from intercourse conducted in the sitting positions. (Of course, you may still get a great deal of pleasure, but, in strict terms of sexual stimulation, your excitement is not likely to reach the peaks you may reach in other positions.) Unless your woman knows a great deal about such matters, she will not know the best ways of stimulating you, she will not have the means of support of her own weight to allow her to perform the movements that allow her to offer you the most intriguing sensations of genital friction, and—in certain cases—she will find difficulty in supporting herself at all unless she is well developed muscularly.

So, to compensate for all these drawbacks, here is a special sexual bonus that can add extra pleasures and intriguing sensations to intercourse in the sitting position.

Start off in Posture #36—preferably in some sort of hard-seated, straight-backed armchair. You are sitting forward on the chair, leaning back somewhat. Your woman is sitting on your knees, facing you. As you approach your climax, grab the arms of the chair and pull yourself up into a standing position. As you do this, your woman should throw her arms about you and fold her legs around yours, so that you can support her in the standing posture you are now taking.

291

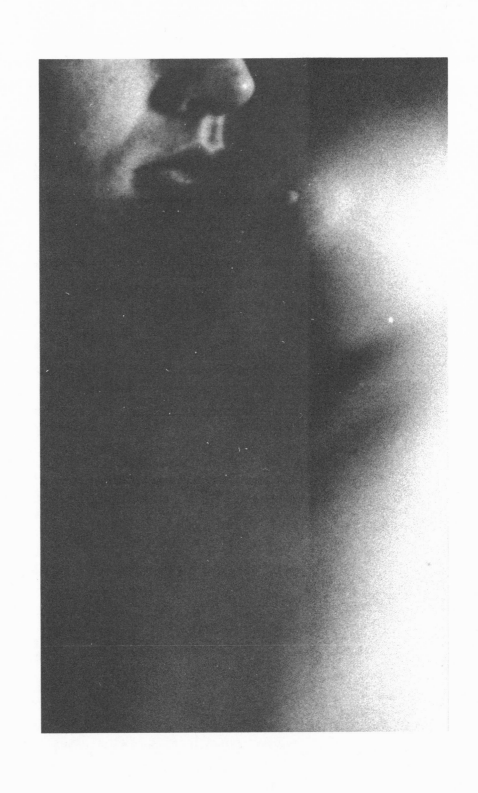

Do all this just as your climax approaches, so that you reach the standing position just as you ejaculate into your woman's vagina.

This movement will add an extra jolt to your orgasm—one that may addict you to this trick.

Of course, you have to be in reasonably good physical shape to accomplish this. And if your woman is a two-ton Betty, you had better forget about trying it. Timing is of supreme importance in the use of this technique: getting up too soon may spoil it for you and waiting too long makes it useless. You may have to try this a few times before you can master it, but the pleasure you will receive from performing this technique correctly will be well worth the effort involved.

10

Sexual Intercourse Positions: part four

The face to face
side positions

Entering the vagina
from the rear

Anal intercourse

EVEN though we have already described 37 different postures for sexual intercourse—and dozens of variations and combinations follow from them—there are still whole groups of positions yet to consider. As you can see, the couple that suffers from boredom because they only know or use just two or three—or even just one—basic positions simply is missing out on an almost infinite range of sexual variety.

THE FACE-TO-FACE- SIDE POSITIONS

These are very good positions in which to begin sexual relations with an inexperienced woman. (Or with any woman, as a matter of fact, if you, yourself, are relatively inexperienced.)

Posture #38 This position is very easy to get into—although movement is rather restricted once you are into it.

First, have the woman lie on her back, bend her legs at the knees, and spread her thighs apart to expose that center of joy between her legs. Now, the man lies over her, supporting himself on his hands and knees. He carefully and gently inserts his penis into her vagina. As you will realize, this is the basic woman-on-her-back posture. But, once penetration is made, the couple immediately shifts into a face-to-face side position.

The woman brings her legs up towards her body until they rest against ahe man's thighs. It is best if she gently, but firmly, presses them inward to lock into the man's body. The couple can then roll over onto one side without losing the genital connection—all the while remaining face to face. Until this roll is completed, neither partner should engage in any movement to cause genital friction, in that this may cause a loss of insertion, especially if the couple is inexperienced.

There are many advantages to this position. The man can pause for as long a time as he finds necessary to control himself without tiring himself (by having to hold himself up above his partner) or falling on his woman and almost smothering her (and actually smothering her sexual excitement).

Second, the angle of insertion of the penis in the vagina is usually just right in this position, and this is very important.

Third, both the man and the woman have their hands free to explore each other's bodies and caress each other all across the areas of the buttocks, the breasts, the back, the thighs, etc. This is very good because both partners can maintain the necessary degree of excitement, without pushing the man too close to the limit of premature climax.

Fourth, this is a very relaxed position, which allows the couple to really get to know each other sexually and allows the man to be gentle and reassuring to his woman if she is young and anxious.

Finally, and also very important, the position is an easy and comfortable one, requiring no acrobatic skills in a couple which, for one reason or another—including health—is not interested in, or ready for, a wild evening of sexual gymnastics.
It is a very good idea for a newly married couple to hold to this side position for a while until they have learned to control their sexual pressure on the man. Because it takes so very little to trigger a man's sexual release, it is essential that

the woman be in close communication with the man and understand his signs that he is approaching climax. It will be necessary for him to maintain pauses in his sexual motions, and in this position he can do so without disengaging and without tiring himself or his woman. Basically, sexual activity can be prolonged almost indefinitely once a couple has learned how to gauge and influence the man's state of sexual excitement.

After all, what satisfaction will a woman receive if she is so self-centered or so ignorant that she does not bother to learn how to read her man's scale of sexual temperature—and how to adjust his sexual thermostat to match hers?

This knowledge of sexual control must be learned as soon as possible, because only then can both partners work toward achieving mutual climax. A few men go directly into a woman-stimulating sexual rhythm without any pause whatsoever. Others find this impossible and have to rely on rebuilding the woman's passion after a necessary pause caused it to sag.

At any rate, the face-to-face side positions—especially this one —are excellent for newly married or inexperienced couples. Why not have as much fun as possible while learning how to master the art of masculine sexual control?

Posture #39 Have your woman lie on her back, with her bottom—from the waist down—twisted over to the right. Then, both of her legs should be folded up, bent at the knee, while her left leg (the upper leg) will be in the air at a bent angle and also, of course, bent at the knee. (You might try placing a pillow under her buttocks to help her in maintaining this twisted position.)

Now, you will approach your woman on your knees and on your side—but still holding your torso off the surface of the bed (or floor) with the aid of your elbow. You will, of course, be facing your woman.

299

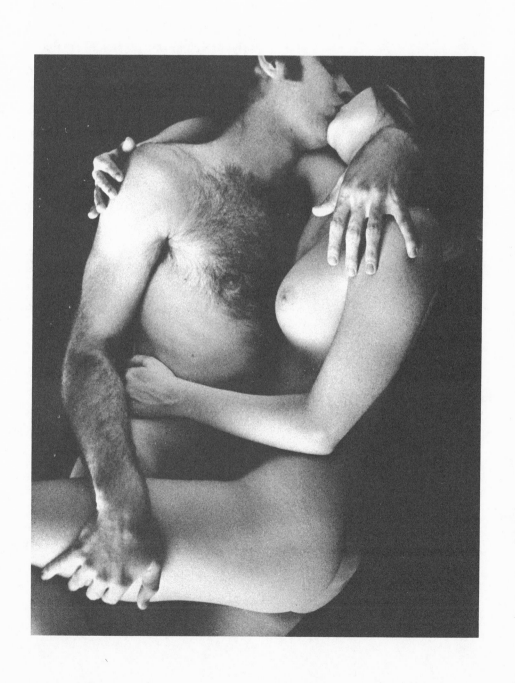

She will then enclose her thighs about your hips, holding your body in a locked position between her legs. If you like, you can now lower your body almost completely onto the bed, resting on your arm and on your legs. Your stomach is resting against your woman's upper thigh.

Posture #40   This position is similar to Posture #39, except that the woman's left leg is stretched out, rather than being bent at the knee. It is held slightly in the air. Actually, she is more nearly stretched out on her back than on her side, although there is still that side twist to her body. As before, her right leg is bent at the knee and held up almost level to her buttocks. In this position, you can be resting on your side, being supported by your two knees, your left arm, and—to a lesser extent—by your woman's soft body.

Remember, though, that your movement in this position is rather restricted because you are both, to a certain extent, pinned down by each other.

Posture #41   Your woman lies in a position similar to that in posture #39: that is, her back is on the ground, the lower part of her body is twisted to the right, with her left buttock in the air and the right leg bent at the knee and flat on its side on the ground. Where this posture differs from Posture #39, however, is that her left leg is pulled right up, the kneecap facing the ceiling.

Because of the nature of the posture she is assuming, you will have to pull up your right knee very sharply so as to approach her for penetration. (Again, you are almost completely on your side, as in Posture #39, resting on your elbow and legs.)

In this position, you will find that you will be able to achieve quite a deep penetration—which is certainly a major advantage of this particular posture.

302

ENTERING THE VAGINA FROM THE REAR

The positions by which you gain entry into your woman's vagina by approaching from behind are used chiefly for variety, for increasing the chances for pregnancy, and for providing a relaxed means of intercourse that still permits a high degree of sexual stimulation and genital friction.

There is a certain social stigma attached to this rear entry approach to intercourse because it is associated in many people's minds with the manner of sexual union used by animal species other than Homo sapiens. This stigma certainly should not exist and you and your woman should disregard it as long as it still exists. Animals use this approach because it is the most natural one for them to use—their organs are in perfect alignment in this position. Well, it should be remembered that human beings are animals, too. And our anatomies are not so radically different from the anatomies of many other mammals. Rear entry positions align the human male and female genitals perfectly, too. If your woman bends over and you approach her from the side of the buttocks, you will be able to see very clearly that your penis is in perfect alignment with her vagina.

Nonetheless, the unhappy fact remains that many people—especially women—do not particularly care for rear entry approaches. Obviously, a central reason for this distaste on the part of many people is the fact that couples generally prefer to face each other when they are making love—and this, of course, is not possible with a vaginal entry from the rear. Nevertheless, the man is usually free to caress his woman in most rear entry positions. And one of the absolutely best, most exciting, positions happens to be a rear entry position.

Note: Postures #21 and #22, described in Chapter 8, involve rear entry, with the man on his back and the woman astride him, facing away.

303

Posture #42 This rather common rear entry position is attained while both partners lie on their sides—the man, obviously, behind the woman and facing her back.

She brings her knees up into a position that is at approximately a right angle to the line of her torso. The man presses up against the woman's back, imitating her position, so that the tops of his thighs are pressed up against the bottoms of hers. Penetration is made in this position.

You will find this to be a very useful position if one of you happens to be ill—or if your wife is pregnant. Both of you have the ability to regulate the depth to which your penis is inserted, merely by the amount your woman crouches forward and the degree to which you arch your body.(Controlling the depth of penetration is especially important when your woman is pregnant.)

Generally speaking, the woman will not be very stimulated in this position—for one thing, her clitoris is completely ignored—and it is to be expected that she will not reach an orgasm. You, on the other hand, will very easily be able to ejaculate. In fact, you can do this even if your partner is so ill that she can barely move.

In this rear entry side position, your woman's buttocks will, of course, interfere with the depth to which you can insert your penis. This can, however, be counteracted—for the man, at any rate. While the woman's buttocks interfere with a deep penetration, they also nearly encircle your penis, replacing the friction lost because of the shallowness of penetration. Thus, all your woman has to do is to tighten the muscles of both buttocks to provide a certain amount of stimulation for your penis. If you have never experienced this sensation before, you will undoubtedly be intrigued by it. And you will be surprised at how quickly she can bring you to the point of ejaculation.

An additional benefit of this rear entry side position, if one of you happens to be sick, is the fact that very little overall body motion is produced.

Posture #43   This particular position—and the two following ones, Posture #44 and #45—are all sometimes called "Riding the Stallion." They all involve the woman bending herself so that her buttocks project out and her torso is approximately parallel with the floor and perpendicular to her upper legs.

In this particular position, she will be bending over a bed, with her knees on the floor and her elbows resting on the bed. You will approach your woman, from behind, on your knees. Now, you can bend somewhat forward as you "mount the stallion," but this will have the effect of pulling your hips backward slightly and you will find difficulty in making a deep penetration—in fact, your penis will not enter very far at all. The only advantage you have in bending forward and pulling your hips backward is that you are putting yourself in a better position to stimulate and caress your wife with your hands, or to kiss her back or her nape or ears.

On the other hand, you can arch your torso backwards somewhat, which has the opposite effect. As you arch yourself backwards, your hips—and penis—press forward, thus assisting you in making a deeper penetration. Of course, you will be less able to caress your wife, but the extra depth will probably be more important to you.

Posture #44   This position is another form of "Riding the Stallion." It is almost exactly the same as Posture #43, except that there is no bed involved now. (At least, it is not involved as a support for her torso. While this position is described as being performed on the floor, it can just as well be performed entirely up on a bed.)

Instead of resting her elbows on a bed, the woman is on the floor on her hands (arms unbent at the elbows) and knees. The man approaches her from behind, on his knees. In this position, it is better for him to arch his body backwards, because—in addition to getting deeper penetration—he should not lean forward while thrusting into his woman or he may well knock her down onto her face.

305

A variation on this position is for the woman's torso to be sloping (head down) toward the floor, instead of being parallel with the floor. This happens if the woman decides to support herself on her forearms instead of on her hands, bending her elbows instead of keeping them straight.

Posture #45 Again, here is yet another way to "Ride the Stallion." In this particular position, the woman stands, legs straight but apart, her body bent forward at the buttocks. She should rest her arms on the edge of a table.

You will approach her from behind, also standing on your feet. Again, you will have the option of arching your body backward to gain a deeper penetration or the option of bending slightly forward and over her to gain the ability to caress her—at the expense of some depth of penetration.

Posture #46 This is a rear entry sitting position. You sit on a chair or bench and your woman sits on top of your thighs, facing away from you. You should be leaning somewhat backward to make your penis accessible to her vagina and she should be leaning somewhat forward to permit a comfortable connection. As with other rear entry positions, the two of you are able to regulate the depth of penetration of the penis to the vagina by adjusting your body angles. The more space between your chest and her back, the greater the depth of penetration. You can decrease the insertion depth by not leaning backwards. She can decrease the insertion depth by not bending forward. To get maximum depth, you lean as far back as possible and she bends as far forward as possible.

Of course, you can vary this position by being on your back on the floor or on a bed, instead of sitting in a chair. In this case, you can lean all the way back and she can lean all the way forward.

Posture #47 Here, your woman lies on her back, with her knees drawn up toward her breasts. You lie at right angles to her, on your side, and insert your penis in her vagina. Once the penetration

308

is complete, you can roll somewhat onto your back—although your buttocks will still be almost in their original position—so that your shoulders and head rest on the bed. Obviously, your body will be somewhat twisted at the waist.

As you shift position, your woman can lower her legs partially onto your upper hip.

You can see that this is not quite the same as other rear entry positions in terms of the way your penis is situated in her vagina. But it is a very pleasant and restful position for both of you. You will be limited to gentle, small movements, but they will prove very stimulating.

It is possible to reach this position from any of several woman-on-her-back postures, without losing your genital connection. For this reason, you may want to try this while resting between rounds of vigorous movement in the woman-on-her-back positions.

Posture #48 This posture is related to Posture #47, but it is a favored relative. In fact, many couples find this to be one of the very best positions for intercourse.

You and your woman lie flat on your backs, next to each other. Your woman is to your right. She draws her knees sharply up toward her torso and you turn toward your woman, lying on your side, facing her.

Now, remaining on your side, you shift your upper body away from your woman until you are lying at right angles to her body, your thighs beneath your woman's legs. So far, you can see that this posture is exactly the same as Posture #47. And you can introduce your penis into your woman at this stage. Now comes the difference.

Because you started out on the left side of your woman, you are lying on your right side. Your left leg is the upper one and your right leg is below, so that your woman's buttocks are resting on your right thigh. Now you put your left leg (the upper one) *between your woman's raised legs*. In this

309

fashion, you bring her right leg downwards, toward your right leg. You are now in this intriguing position, ready for a long session of delightful sensations. You are now making almost a complete rear entry and your legs are intertwined as they are in no other position. Your right leg is on bottom; her right leg is above it; your left leg is above that; and her left leg is on top.

In this position, you will find your movements severely limited, but both of you will get immense pleasure from the movement that is possible. Because you are in a relaxed posture and are not performing vigorous movements, you should be able to hold off your orgasm as long as necessary. On the other hand, the sensations in this position are so intriguing and exciting—especially for the woman—that you can expect your woman to reach her climax rather soon.

Some couples may be bothered by the fact that their upper torsos and heads are so far apart, but, of course, this distance helps make this position ideal for hot nights when vigorous motion and close bodily contact may be too much.

These, then, are the rear entry positions (even though the last two are extremely modified versions). Be sure that you and your woman try them—even if your woman has an initial reluctance to engage in intercourse in which you enter her vagina from the rear.

ANAL INTERCOURSE

Of all the techniques in this book, anal intercourse is the least socially acceptable. It is even illegal in some states and there is some question as to the medical wisdom of introducing an object as big as a penis into a woman's anus. Beyond this, there are taboos against anal intercourse, based on the idea that the anus is a "dirty" part of the body. And some men who have anxieties about their masculinity reject the idea of performing this because they associate the act with homosexuals—who do, indeed, commonly rely on anal intercourse as a basic sexual technique.

For all these reasons, the author is definitely not recommending that anybody practice anal intercourse. It is up to you to weigh the medical, legal, and psychological factors and come to your own decision. The following positions, therefore, are included only for the benefit of those who have already decided to try anal intercourse.

These positions have several advantages—beside lending greater variety to a couple's sex life.

First, they may prove useful at times when there are medical reasons to avoid vaginal intercourse, but when sexual stimulation is acceptable and desired.

Second, they are quite pleasurable to the man, in that the anus grasps the inserted penis firmly and softly, with a power and tightness not usually possible in the vagina.

Third, many women reach orgasm very quickly during anal intercourse, because of the great physical and emotional stimulation.

Posture #49 This is the basic position for anal intercourse.
The woman lies face down on a bed, with her legs spread but her knees unbent.

Before approaching her, the man must be well lubricated. One way to do this is to use lubrication from the vagina, but the surest thing is artificial lubrication. (Some of the commercial lubricants may also be applied to the entrance of the woman, if you wish.) This is very important, in that you can cause pain and injury by introducing an unlubricated penis into the anus.

Now, the man lies down over the woman, so that his penis is in the crack between her buttocks and between her thighs. The woman should become completely relaxed. The anal muscles, especially, should be relaxed. Then, raising himself

311

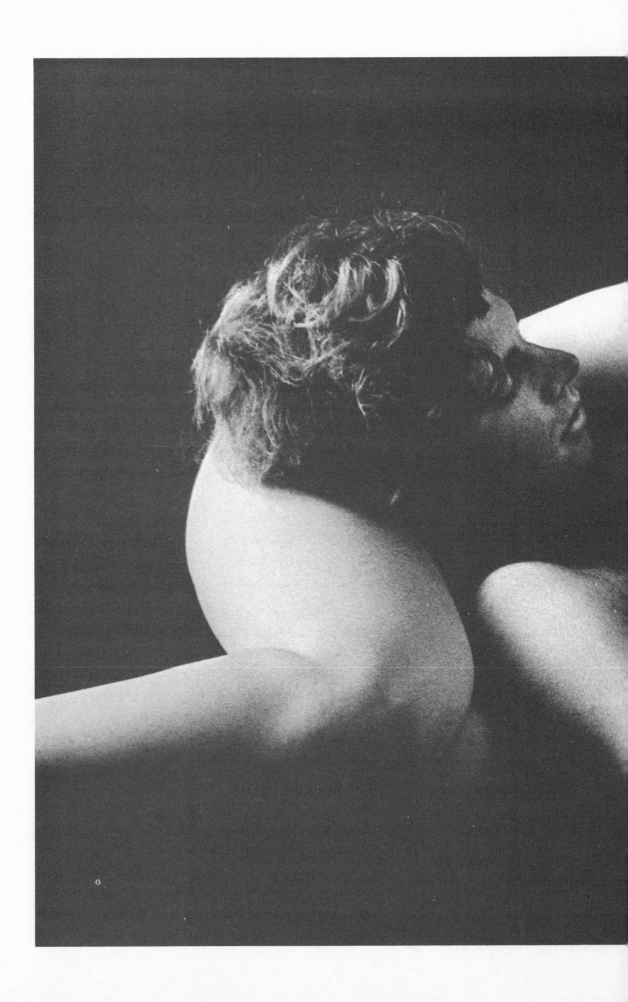

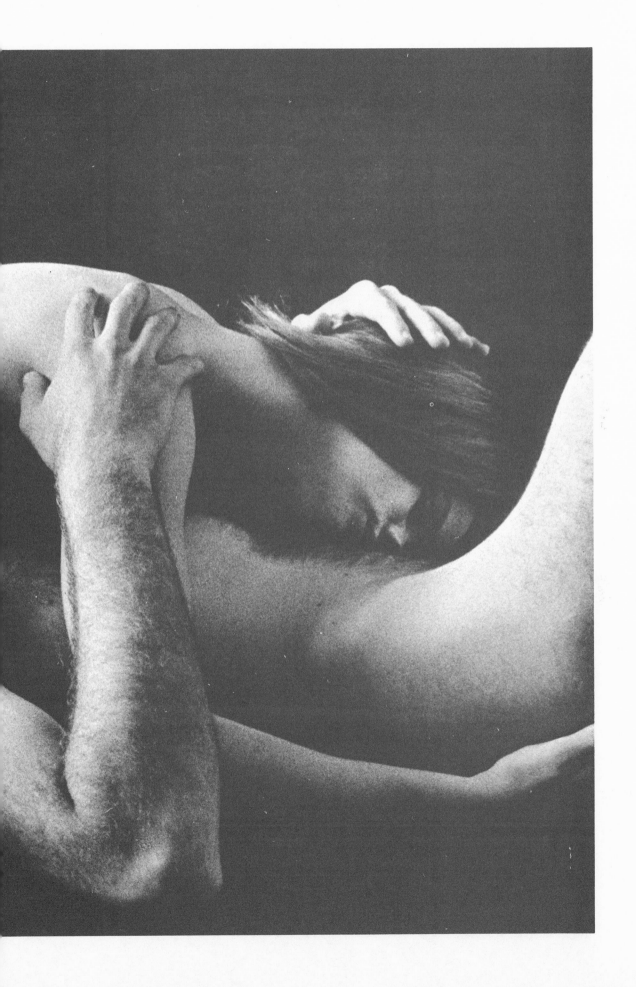

on his hands and knees, the man can begin to introduce his penis into the woman's rear opening. If it makes it easier, either the man or the woman can guide the penis in, by hand. Entrance must be made at the pace the woman indicates. In point of fact, all movement should be according to the woman's expressed wishes.

After penetration is complete, the couple shifts position somewhat, in order to lock the penis tightly into the woman's anus. Slowly, the woman brings her legs together and the man brings his legs up onto the woman's legs. He may remain in this position, providing that he carries most of his weight on his arms. But it is better for the man to slide his knees down off the woman's legs, ending up in a hands and knees position *with the woman's legs between the man's knees,* which are securely planted on the bed on either side of the woman.

At first—after penetration and this position switch have been completed—it is best if the man doesn't move. The woman can rotate her hips to achieve the friction she wants, and this will be quite pleasant for the man, because of the delightful sensation of the woman's buttocks grinding against his lower belly. Only after the woman has become very relaxed and comfortable, should the man begin his careful movements. These should be rotating, rather than up and down, although a slight up and down motion may eventually be possible without hurting the woman.

Posture #50   In this position, the woman lies flat on her back, with her knees pulled very sharply up to her breast, and then spread as wide as possible to make the crotch completely exposed and accessible. The woman will have to hold her legs in this position, and it may help to put a pillow under the upper section of her buttocks. The whole point, of course, is to make the anal opening available for penetration.

Well lubricated, the man approaches his woman on his knees,

body erect. The man can lift the woman's buttocks higher than they already are if he needs to in order to penetrate the anus. If this is not necessary, his hands will be free to stimulate the woman's clitoris and vagina while the couple is engaged in anal intercourse.

In this position, the man will have to be very careful not to hurt his woman with his movements.

Posture #51 Either the basic man-on-his-back, woman sitting on him position or the man-sitting, woman sitting on him (facing away) position can be adapted to anal intercourse.

11

Your Sexual Motions

ONE final comment on the motions you use in sexual intercourse: Generally, it is the natural instinct of men to make short, sharp in-and-out motions with their penis. However, it will be found that a long, slow stroke is immensely more satisfying, because slow steady rhythms are better suited to the building of excitement in women and also because the slower, steadier stroke allows the woman to more easily supplement your movements with her own movements—which means increased satisfaction for both of you. In this way, sexual stimulation comes in a gradual and overwhelming wave, instead of a short and less satisfactory burst.

One more point to consider: It is important for you to realize that the penis should be used as a stimulator, as a creator of friction—before and during intercourse. With this in mind, always remember that—if the position permits—your penis should be lifted against the clitoris during intercourse.

Thus, never forget that the entire shaft of the penis can and should be used to generate passion. Make use of it!

And a parting bit of advice: Enjoy yourself!